CAP 413

RADIOTELEPHONY MANUAL

CIVIL AVIATION AUTHORITY, LONDON, JANUARY 2001

ISBN 0 86039 809 9

First published September 1978
Second edition April 1984
Third edition August 1992
Fourth edition January 1994
Fifth edition January 1995
Sixth edition January 1996
Seventh edition December 1996
Eighth edition January 1998
Ninth edition January 1999
Tenth edition January 2000
Eleventh edition January 2001

Printed and distributed by
Westward documedia Limited, 37 Windsor Street, Cheltenham, England

Foreword

STATUS

This publication is based on the International Standards and Recommended Practices contained in ICAO Annex 10 Volume 2 (Communications Procedures) to the Convention on International Civil Aviation and the PANS-RAC (Procedures for Air Navigation Services, Rules of the Air and Air Traffic Services) Doc 4444 – Part X.

It is a useful reference book for the examination for the Flight Radiotelephony Operator's (Restricted) Licence. Current operational details are to be found in the United Kingdom AIP, however, air traffic controllers, flight information officers and aeronautical radio station operators should refer to Manual of Air Traffic Services (CAP 493), Manual of Flight Information Services (CAP 410) and Aeronautical Radio Station Operators' Guide (CAP 452) respectively for comprehensive instructions on phraseology to be used by aeronautical ground radio stations. Candidates for JAA professional pilot and instrument rating examinations, which were introduced on 1 January 1999, should note that the 'Communications' examination syllabus is based on ICAO Annex 10 Vol 2 and Doc 9432–AN/925 Manual of Radiotelephony, and not CAP 413.

Major changes to RT phraseology will be notified in Aeronautical Information Circulars (AICs); updated versions of this Manual will be published at regular intervals. Users of this manual who do not already have access to AICs may wish to consider subscribing to the AIC Amendment Service in order to maintain the currency of this publication. Details of this service may be obtained from the CAA at the address shown in the Bibliography at page 181.

FORMAT

The examples of phraseology in this handbook are intended to be representative of radiotelephony procedures in common use. The initial call in a series of messages in Chapters 2–11 inclusive always appear on the left hand side of the page; remaining messages connected with the subject of the initial call appear in chronological order on the right hand side.

The agency making the transmission is identified by the colour background of the example phraseology as follows:

> AIRCRAFT

> GROUND STATION (ATC, FIS, A/G)

> VEHICLE

While the procedures and phraseologies specifically reflect the situation in an environment where Very High Frequency (VHF) is in use, they are equally applicable in those areas where High Frequency (HF) is used. In the latter case a strict adherence to procedures is considered essential because of the greater interference potential and in many cases poor reception resulting from the propagation characteristics of certain frequency bands.

Enquiries regarding the text of this publication should be addressed to:

Manager Projects
ATS Standards Department
2W
Aviation House
Gatwick Airport South
West Sussex RH6 0YR

Table of Contents

Chapter 1 – Glossary

1.1   DEFINITIONS

Absolute Minimum   The calculated RVR, or at aerodromes where RVR measurements are not taken or available, the visibility, which is the lowest possible for any instrument approach to be made using that particular approach aid.

Advisory Area   A designated area where air traffic advisory service is available.

Advisory Route   A designated route along which air traffic advisory service is available.

Aerodrome   Any area of land or water designed, equipped, set apart or commonly used for affording facilities for the landing and departure of aircraft.

Aerodrome Control Service   Air traffic control service for aerodrome traffic.

Aerodrome Traffic   All traffic on the manoeuvring area of an aerodrome and all aircraft operating in the vicinity of an aerodrome.

Aerodrome Traffic Zone   Airspace of defined dimensions established around an aerodrome for the protection of aerodrome traffic.

Aeronautical Mobile Service   A radio communication service between aircraft stations and aeronautical stations, or between aircraft stations.

Aeronautical Station   A land station in the aeronautical mobile service. In certain instances, an aeronautical station may be placed on board a ship or an earth satellite.

Airborne Collision Avoidance System   An aircraft system based on SSR transponder signals which operates independently of ground-based equipment to provide advice to the pilot on potential conflicting aircraft that are equipped with SSR transponders.

Aircraft Station   A mobile station in the aeronautical mobile service on board an aircraft.

1

Air-ground Communications   Two-way communication between aircraft and stations or locations on the surface of the earth.

AIRPROX   A situation in which, in the opinion of a pilot or controller, the distance between aircraft as well as their relative positions and speed have been such that the safety of the aircraft involved was or may have been compromised.

Air Traffic   All aircraft in flight or operating on the manoeuvring area of an aerodrome.

Air Traffic Control Clearance   Authorisation for an aircraft to proceed under conditions specified by an air traffic control unit.

Air Traffic Service (ATS)   A generic term meaning variously, flight information service, alerting service, air traffic advisory service, air traffic control service, area control service, approach control service or aerodrome control service.

Airway   A control area or part of a control area established in the form of a corridor equipped with radio navigation aids.

Altitude   The vertical distance of a level, a point or an object considered as a point, measured from mean sea level.

Area Control Centre   A term used in the United Kingdom to describe a unit providing en-route air traffic control services.

Automatic Terminal Information Service (ATIS) (UK)   The provision of current, routine information to arriving and departing aircraft by means of continuous and repetitive broadcasts throughout the day or a specified portion of the day.

Base Turn   A turn executed by the aircraft during the initial approach between the end of the outboard track and the beginning of the intermediate or final approach track. The tracks are not reciprocal.

Blind Transmission   A transmission from one station to another station in circumstances where two-way communication cannot be established but where it is believed that the called station is able to receive the transmission.

Broadcast   A transmission of information relating to air navigation that is not addressed to a specific station or stations.

Clearance Limit   The point to which an aircraft is granted an air traffic control clearance.

Control Area   A controlled airspace extending upwards from a specified limit above the surface of the earth.

Controlled Airspace   An airspace of defined dimensions within which air traffic control service is provided in accordance with the airspace classification.

Control Zone   A controlled airspace extending upwards from the surface of the earth to a specified upper limit.

Cruising Level   A level maintained during a significant portion of a flight.

Decision Altitude/Height   A specified altitude/height in a precision approach at which a missed approach must be initiated if the required visual reference to continue the approach to land has not been established.

Elevation   The vertical distance of a point or level on, or affixed to, the surface of the earth measured from mean sea level.

Estimated Time of Arrival   The time at which the pilot estimates that the aircraft will be over a specific location.

Flight Level   A surface of constant atmospheric pressure, which is related to a specific pressure datum, 1013.2 mb, and is separated from other such surfaces by specific pressure intervals.

Flight Plan   Specified information provided to air traffic services units, relative to an intended flight or portion of a flight of an aircraft. Flight Plans fall into two categories: Full Flight Plans and Abbreviated Flight Plans.

General Air Traffic   Flights operating in accordance with civil air traffic procedures.

Heading   The direction in which the longitudinal axis of an aircraft is pointed, usually expressed in degrees from North (magnetic).

Height   The vertical distance of a level, a point, or an object considered as a point measured from a specified datum.

IFR Flight   A flight conducted in accordance with the instrument flight rules.

Instrument Meteorological Conditions (IMC)   Meteorological conditions expressed in terms of visibility, horizontal and vertical distance from cloud, less than the minima specified for visual meteorological conditions.

Known Traffic   Traffic, the current flight details and intentions of which are known to the controller concerned through direct communication or co-ordination.

Level   A generic term relating to the vertical position of an aircraft in flight and meaning variously, height, altitude or flight level.

Minimum Descent Altitude/Height   A altitude/height in a non-precision or circling approach below which descent may not be made without visual reference.

Missed Approach Point (MAPt)   The point in an instrument approach procedure at or before which the prescribed missed approach procedure must be initiated in order to ensure that the minimum obstacle clearance is not infringed.

Missed Approach Procedure   The procedure to be followed if the approach cannot be continued.

Procedure Turn   A manoeuvre in which a turn is made away from a designated track followed by a turn in the opposite direction to permit the aircraft the aircraft to intercept and proceed along the reciprocal of the designated track.

Radar Approach   An approach, executed by an aircraft, under the direction of a radar controller.

Radar Contact   The situation which exists when the radar blip or radar position symbol of a particular aircraft is seen and identified on a radar display.

Radar Identification   The process of correlating a particular radar blip or radar position symbol with a specific aircraft.

Radar Vectoring   Provision of navigational guidance to aircraft in the form of specific headings, based on the use of radar.

Reporting Point   A specified geographical location in relation to which the position of an aircraft can be reported.

Runway   A defined rectangular area on a land aerodrome prepared for the landing and take-off of aircraft.

Runway Visual Range   The range over which the pilot of an aircraft on the centre line of a runway can expect to see the runway surface markings, or the lights delineating the runway or identifying its centre line.

Signal Area   An area on an aerodrome used for the display of ground signals.

Special VFR Flight   A flight made at any time in a control zone which is Class A airspace or is in any other control zone in IMC or at night, in respect of which the appropriate air traffic control unit has given permission for the flight to be made in accordance with special instructions given by that unit, instead of in accordance with the Instrument Flight Rules and in the course of which flight the aircraft complies with any instructions given by that unit and remains clear of cloud and in sight of the surface.

Straight Ahead   When used in departure clearances means: 'track extended runway centre-line'.

When given in Missed Approach Procedures means: 'continue on Final Approach Track'.

Terminal Control Area   A control area normally established at the confluence of airways in the vicinity of one or more major aerodromes.

Threshold   The beginning of that portion of the runway useable for landing.

Traffic Alert and Collision Avoidance System   See ACAS.

VFR Flight   A flight conducted in accordance with the visual flight rules.

Visual Meteorological Conditions (VMC)   Meteorological conditions expressed in terms of visibility, horizontal and vertical distance from cloud, equal to or better than specified minima.

1.2   COMMONLY USED ABBREVIATIONS

1.2.1   The abbreviations annotated with an asterisk are normally spoken as complete words. The remainder are normally spoken using the constituent letters rather than the spelling alphabet.

A

aal	Above Aerodrome Level
ACAS*	Airborne Collision Avoidance System (pronounced A-kas) (see TCAS)
ACC	Area Control Centre
ADF	Automatic Direction-Finding Equipment
ADR	Advisory Route
ADT	Approved Departure Time
AFTN	Aeronautical Fixed Telecommunication Network
AFIS	Aerodrome Flight Information Service
agl	Above Ground Level
AAIB	Air Accident Investigation Branch
AIC	Aeronautical Information Circular
AIRPROX*	Aircraft Proximity (replaces Airmiss/APHAZ)
AIP	Aeronautical Information Publication
AIS	Aeronautical Information Services
amsl	Above Mean Sea Level
ANO	Air Navigation Order
APAPI	Abbreviated Precision Approach Path Indicator (pronounced Ay-PAPI)
ATA	Actual Time of Arrival
ATC	Air Traffic Control (in general)
ATD	Actual Time of Departure
ATIS*	Automatic Terminal Information Service
ATS	Air Traffic Service
ATSU	Air Traffic Service Unit
AT-VASIS	Abbreviated T Visual Approach Slope Indicator System (pronounced Ay-Tee-VASIS)
ATZ	Aerodrome Traffic Zone

C

CAA	Civil Aviation Authority
CAVOK*	Visibility, cloud and present weather better than prescribed values or conditions (CAVOK pronounced Cav-okay)
CTA	Control Area
CTR	Control Zone

D

DAAIS*	Danger Area Activity Information Service (DAAIS pronounced DAY-ES)
DACS*	Danger Area Crossing Service
DF	Direction Finding
DME	Distance Measuring Equipment
DR	Dead Reckoning

E

EAT	Expected Approach Time
ETA	Estimated Time of Arrival
ETD	Estimated Time of Departure

F

FAF	Final Approach Fix
FIR	Flight Information Region
FIS	Flight Information Service
FL	Flight Level
ft	Foot (feet)

G

GAT	General Air Traffic
GLONASS*	Global Orbiting Navigation Satellite System (pronounced Glo-NAS)
GMC	Ground Movement Control
GNSS	Global Navigation Satellite System
GPS	Global Positioning System

H

H24	Continuous day and night service (H24 pronounced Aitch Twenty Fower)
HF	High Frequency
HN	Sunset to Sunrise
HJ	Sunrise to Sunset

I

IAF	Initial Approach Fix
ICAO*	International Civil Aviation Organisation
IF	Intermediate Approach Fix
IFR	Instrument Flight Rules
ILS	Instrument Landing System
IMC	Instrument Meteorological Conditions
IRVR	Instrumented Runway Visual Range

K

kg	Kilogramme(s)
km	Kilometre(s)
kt	Knot(s)

M

MAPt	Missed Approach Point
MATZ*	Military Aerodrome Traffic Zone

MDA/H	Minimum Descent Altitude/Height
MEDA*	Military Emergency Diversion Aerodrome
MET*	Meteorological or Meteorology
METAR*	Routine aviation aerodrome weather report
mb	Millibars

N

NATS	National Air Traffic Services
NDB	Non-Directional Radio Beacon

O

OAC	Oceanic Area Control Unit
OCA	Oceanic Control Area
OCA/H	Obstacle Clearance Altitude/Height

P

PAPI*	Precision Approach Path Indicator (pronounced PAPI)
PAR	Precision Approach Radar

Q

QDM	Magnetic heading (zero wind) (Sometimes employed to indicate magnetic heading of a runway)
QDR	Magnetic bearing
QFE	The observed pressure at a specified datum (usually aerodrome or runway threshold elevation) corrected for temperature
QGH	Ground interpreted letdown procedure using DF equipment
QNE	Landing altimeter setting
QNH	Altimeter sub-scale setting to obtain elevation when on the ground and indications of elevation when in the air
QTE	True Bearing

R

RA	Resolution Advisory (see TCAS)
RCC	Rescue Co-ordination Centre
RPS	Regional Pressure Setting
RT	Radiotelephone/Radiotelephony
RVR	Runway Visual Range

S

SAR	Search and Rescue
SID*	Standard Instrument Departure

SIGMET*	Significant information concerning en-route weather phenomena which may affect the safety of aircraft operations
SRA	Surveillance Radar Approach
SSR	Secondary Surveillance Radar
STAR*	Standard Instrument Arrival

T

TA	Traffic Advisory (see TCAS)
TAF*	Terminal Aerodrome Forecast
TCAS*	Traffic Alert and Collision Avoidance System (pronounced Tee-kas) (see ACAS)
TMA	Terminal Control Area
T-VASIS	T Visual Approach Slope Indicator System (pronounced TEE-VASIS)

U

UAS	Upper Airspace
UHF	Ultra-High Frequency
UIR	Upper Flight Information Region
UTC	Co-ordinated Universal Time

V

VASIS*	Visual Approach Slope Indicator System (pronounced VASIS)
VDF	Very High Frequency Direction-Finding Station
VFR	Visual Flight Rules
VHF	Very High Frequency (30 to 300 MHz)
VMC	Visual Meteorological Conditions
VOLMET*	Meteorological information for aircraft in flight
VOR	VHF Omnidirectional Radio Range
VORTAC*	VOR and TACAN combination

1.3 HOURS OF SERVICE AND COMMUNICATIONS WATCH

1.3.1 The hours of service of the radio facilities available in the United Kingdom are published in the UK AIP (ENR and AD) which also details those periods set aside for maintenance.

1.3.2 When an aircraft has established communication with an ATSU it is required to maintain a listening watch with that ATSU and advise the ATSU when the listening watch is about to cease. Aircraft should not cease to maintain a listening watch, except for reasons of safety, without informing the ATSU concerned. A time at which it is expected that the watch will be resumed must be stated.

1.4 RECORD OF COMMUNICATIONS

1.4.1 All ATC units have automatic equipment to record air-ground communications and some other ATS units (eg AFIS) also have such equipment. At those ATS units which do not have automatic recording a written record is kept.

1.5 CATEGORIES OF MESSAGE

1.5.1 The categories of messages handled by the aeronautical mobile service are in the following order of priority:

(a)	Distress messages	See Chapter 9 – Emergency RT Procedures
(b)	Urgency messages	
(c)	Communications relating to direction finding	See Chapter 7 para 7.7
(d)	Flight safety messages	See Chapter 11 para 11.6
(e)	Meteorological messages	See Chapter 10
(f)	Flight Regularity messages	See Chapter 11 para 11.6

Chapter 2 – General Operating Procedures

2.1 INTRODUCTION

2.1.1 Radiotelephony provides the means by which pilots and ground personnel communicate with each other. Used properly, the information and instructions transmitted are of vital importance in assisting in the safe and expeditious operation of aircraft. However, the use of non-standard procedures and phraseology can cause misunderstanding. Incidents and accidents have occurred in which a contributing factor has been the misunderstanding caused by the use of non-standard phraseology. *The importance of using correct and precise standard phraseology cannot be over-emphasised.*

2.2 TRANSMITTING TECHNIQUE

2.2.1 The following transmitting techniques will assist in ensuring that transmitted speech is clearly and satisfactorily received.

   (a) Before transmitting check that the receiver volume is set at the optimum level and listen out on the frequency to be used to ensure that there will be no interference with a transmission from another station.

   (b) Be familiar with microphone operating techniques and do not turn your head away from it whilst talking or vary the distance between it and your mouth. Severe distortion of speech may arise from:

   (i) talking too close to the microphone

   (ii) touching the microphone with the lips

   (iii) holding the microphone or boom (of a combined headset/microphone system).

   (c) Use a normal conversation tone, speak clearly and distinctly.

   (d) Maintain an even rate of speech not exceeding 100 words per minute. When it is known that elements of the message will be written down by the recipients, speak at a slightly slower rate.

(e)   Maintain the speaking volume at a constant level.

(f)   A slight pause before and after numbers will assist in making them easier to understand.

(g)   Avoid using hesitation sounds such as 'er'.

(h)   Depress the transmit switch fully before speaking and do not release it until the message is complete. This will ensure that the entire message is transmitted. However, do not depress transmit switch until ready to speak.

(i)   Be aware that the mother tongue of the person receiving the message may not be English. Therefore, speak clearly and use standard radiotelephony (RT) words and phrases wherever possible.

2.2.2   One of the most irritating and potentially dangerous situations in radiotelephony is a 'stuck' microphone button. Operators should always ensure that the button is released after a transmission and the microphone placed in an appropriate place that will ensure that it will not inadvertently be switched on.

2.3   TRANSMISSION OF LETTERS

2.3.1   The words in the table below shall be used when individual letters are required to be transmitted. The syllables to be emphasised are underlined.

Letter	Word	Appropriate pronunciation
A	Alpha	<u>AL</u> FAH
B	Bravo	BRAH <u>VOH</u>
C	Charlie	<u>CHAR</u> LEE
D	Delta	<u>DELL</u> TAH
E	Echo	<u>ECK</u> OH
F	Foxtrot	<u>FOKS</u> TROT

Letter	Word	Appropriate pronunciation
G	Golf	GOLF
H	Hotel	HOH TELL
I	India	IN DEE AH
J	Juliett	JEW LEE ETT
K	Kilo	KEY LOH
L	Lima	LEE MAH
M	Mike	MIKE
N	November	NO VEM BER
O	Oscar	OSS CAH
P	Papa	PAH PAH
Q	Quebec	KEH BECK
R	Romeo	ROW ME OH
S	Sierra	SEE AIR RAH
T	Tango	TANG GO
U	Uniform	YOU NEE FORM
V	Victor	VIK TAH
W	Whiskey	WISS KEY
X	X-ray	ECKS RAY
Y	Yankee	YANG KEE
Z	Zulu	ZOO LOO

2.4   TRANSMISSION OF NUMBERS

2.4.1   The syllables to be emphasised are underlined.

Numeral or numeral element	Latin alphabet representation
0	ZERO
1	WUN
2	TOO
3	TREE
4	FOWER
5	FIFE
6	SIX
7	SEVEN
8	AIT
9	NINER
Decimal	DAYSEEMAL
Hundred	HUN DRED
Thousand	TOUSAND

2.4.2   All numbers, except those contained in paragraph 2.4.2(b) shall be transmitted by pronouncing each digit separately as follows:

(a)   When transmitting messages containing aircraft callsigns, altimeter settings, flight levels (with the exception of FL 100 which is expressed at 'Flight Level WUN HUN DRED'), headings, wind speeds/directions, transponder codes and frequencies, each digit shall be transmitted separately; examples of this convention are as follows:

Number	Transmitted as	Pronounced as
BAW246	Speedbird Two Four Six	SPEEDBIRD TOO FOWER SIX
FL 100	Flight Level One Hundred	FLIGHT LEVEL WUN HUN DRED
FL 180	Flight Level One Eight Zero	FLIGHT LEVEL WUN AIT ZERO
150 Degrees	One Five Zero Degrees	WUN FIFE ZERO DEGREES
18 Knots	One Eight Knots	WUN AIT KNOTS
122.1	One Two Two Decimal One	WUN TOO TOO DAYSEEMAL WUN
6500	Six Five Zero Zero	SIX FIFE ZERO ZERO (SQUAWK)

(b)   All numbers used in the transmission of altitude, height, cloud height, visibility and runway visual range information which contain whole hundreds and whole thousands shall be transmitted by pronouncing each digit in the number of hundreds or thousands followed by the word HUNDRED or TOUSAND as appropriate. Combinations of thousands and whole hundreds shall be transmitted by pronouncing each digit in the number of thousands followed by the word THOUSAND and the number of hundreds followed by the word HUNDRED; examples of this convention are as follows:

Number	Transmitted as	Pronounced as
10	One Zero	WUN ZERO
100	One Hundred	WUN HUN DRED
2 500	Two Thousand Five Hundred	TOO TOUSAND FIFE HUNDRED
11 000	One One Thousand	WUN WUN TOUSAND
25 000	Two Five Thousand	TOO FIFE TOUSAND

2.4.3   Numbers containing a decimal point shall be transmitted as prescribed in 2.4.1 with the decimal point in appropriate sequence being indicated by the word decimal.

Number	Transmitted as	Pronounced as
118.1	One One Eight Decimal One	WUN WUN AIT DAY SEE MAL WUN
120.375	One Two Zero Decimal Three Seven	WUN TOO ZERO DAY SEE MAL TREE SEVEN

Note: Only the first five figures are used when identifying frequencies separated by 25 kHz.

2.4.4   When it is necessary to verify the accurate reception of numbers the person transmitting the message shall request the person receiving the message to read back the numbers.

2.5   TRANSMISSION OF TIME

2.5.1   When transmitting time, only the minutes of the hour are normally required. However, the hour should be included if there is any possibility of confusion. Time checks shall be given to the nearest minute. Co-ordinated Universal Time (UTC) is to be used at all times, unless specified. 2400 hours designates midnight, the end of the day, and 0000 hours the beginning of the day.

Number	Transmitted as	Pronounced as
0823	Two Three or Zero Eight Two Three	TOO TREE (or ZERO AIT TOO TREE)
1300	One Three Zero Zero	WUN TREE ZERO ZERO
2057	Five Seven or Two Zero Five Seven	FIFE SEVEN (or TOO ZERO FIFE SEVEN)

2.6 STANDARD WORDS AND PHRASES

2.6.1 The following words and phrases shall be used in radiotelephony communications as appropriate and shall have the meaning given below:

Word/Phrase	Meaning
ACKNOWLEDGE	Let me know that you have received and understood this message.
AFFIRM	Yes
APPROVED	Permission for proposed action granted.
BREAK	Indicates the separation between messages.
CANCEL	Annul the previously transmitted clearance.
CHANGING TO	I intend to call . . . (unit) on . . . (frequency)
CHECK	Examine a system or procedure (no answer is normally expected).
CLEARED	Authorised to proceed under the conditions specified.
CLIMB	Climb and maintain
CONFIRM	Have I correctly received the following ...? or Did you correctly receive this message?
CONTACT	Establish radio contact with ... (your details have been passed)
CORRECT	That is correct.
CORRECTION	An error has been made in this transmission (or message indicated). The correct version is ...
DESCEND	Descend and maintain
DISREGARD	Consider that transmission as not sent.
FREECALL	Call . . . (unit) (your details have not been passed – mainly used by military ATC)
HOW DO YOU READ	What is the readability of my transmission.
I SAY AGAIN	I repeat for clarity or emphasis.
MONITOR	Listen out on (frequency).

Word/Phrase	Meaning
NEGATIVE	No; or Permission not granted; or That is not correct.
OVER*	My transmission is ended and I expect a response from you.
OUT*	This exchange of transmissions is ended and no response is expected.
PASS YOUR MESSAGE	Proceed with your message.
READ BACK	Repeat all, or the specified part, of this message back to me exactly as received.
REPORT	Pass requested information.
REQUEST	I should like to know ... or I wish to obtain ...
ROGER	I have received all your last transmission. *Note: Under no circumstances to be used in reply to a question requiring a direct answer in the affirmative (AFFIRM) or negative (NEGATIVE).*
SAY AGAIN	Repeat all, or the following part of your last transmission.
SPEAK SLOWER	Reduce your rate of speech.
STANDBY	Wait and I will call you. *Note: No onward clearance to be assumed.*
VERIFY	Check and confirm.
WILCO	I understand your message and will comply with it (abbreviation for will comply)
WORDS TWICE	*As a request:* Communication is difficult. Please send every word twice. *As Information:* Since communication is difficult, every word in this message will be sent twice.

* Not normally used in U/VHF Communications.

2.7   COMMUNICATIONS

2.7.1   Callsigns for aeronautical stations

2.7.1.1   Aeronautical stations are identified by the name of the location followed by a suffix. The suffix indicates the type of service being provided.

Service	Suffix
Area Control	CONTROL
Radar (in general)	RADAR
Approach Control	APPROACH
Aerodrome Control	TOWER
Approach Control Radar Arrivals/Departures	DIRECTOR/DEPARTURE (RADAR – when tasks combined)/ARRIVALS – (when approved))
Ground Movement Control	GROUND
Precision Approach Radar	TALKDOWN (Military – FINAL CONTROLLER)
Flight Information	INFORMATION
Aerodrome Air/Ground Communications	RADIO
Ground Movement Planning	DELIVERY

2.7.1.2   There are three main categories of aeronautical communications service:

Air traffic control service (ATC) which can only be provided by licensed Air Traffic Control Officers who are closely regulated by the CAA.

Flight information service at aerodromes can be provided only by licensed Flight Information Service Officers (FISOs), who are also regulated by the CAA.

Aerodrome air/ground communications service (A/G) which can be provided by Radio Operators who are not licensed but have obtained a certificate of competency to operate radio equipment on aviation frequencies from the CAA. These operations come under the jurisdiction of the radio license holder, but are not regulated in any other way.

It is an offence to use a callsign for a purpose other than that for which it has been notified.

2.7.1.3 When satisfactory communication has been established, and provided that it will *not be confusing*, the name of the location or the callsign suffix may be omitted.

2.7.2 Aircraft Callsigns

2.7.2.1 When establishing communication an aircraft shall use the full callsigns of both stations.

| Borton Tower G-ABCD | G-ABCD Borton Tower |

2.7.2.2 After satisfactory communication has been established and provided that no confusion is likely to occur, the ground station may abbreviate callsigns (see table below). A pilot may *only* abbreviate the callsign of his aircraft if it has *first* been abbreviated by the aeronautical ground station.

Full callsign	Abbreviation
GBFRM	G-RM
Speedbird GBGDC	Speedbird DC
N31029	N029
N753DA	N3DA
Midland 120	No abbreviation
* Piper GBSZT	Piper ZT

* The name of either the aircraft manufacturers or name of aircraft model may be used as a prefix to the callsign.

2.7.2.3 An aircraft should request the service required on initial contact when freecalling a ground station.

> Westbury Approach, G-ABCD
> request Lower Airspace
> Radar Service

> Wrayton Control, G-ABCD I
> wish to file an airborne flight
> plan

2.7.2.4 An aircraft shall not change its callsign type during a flight. *However,* where there is a likelihood that confusion may occur because of similar callsigns, an aircraft may be instructed by an air traffic service unit (ATSU) to change the type of its callsign temporarily.

2.7.2.5 Aircraft in the heavy wake vortex category shall include the word 'HEAVY' immediately after the aircraft callsign in the initial call to each ATSU.

2.7.3 Continuation of Communications

2.7.3.1 When satisfactory communication has been established, and providing it will not be confusing, the location of the ground station, its suffix or both may be omitted.

2.7.3.2 The placement of the callsigns of both the aircraft and the ground station *within* an established RT exchange should be as follows:

Ground to Air: Aircraft callsign – message or reply.

Air to Ground:

(a) Initiation of new information/request etc – Aircraft callsign then message;

(b) Reply – Repeat of pertinent information/readback/ acknowledgement then aircraft callsign.

G-ABCD descend FL 80	Descend FL 80 G-ABCD
	G-ABCD maintaining FL 80
	G-CD
G-ABCD request descent	G-CD descend FL 40
	Descend FL 40 G-CD

2.7.3.3   When it is considered that reception is likely to be difficult, important elements of the message should be spoken twice.

2.7.3.4   When a ground station wishes to broadcast information to all aircraft likely to receive it, the message should be prefaced by the call 'All stations'.

All stations Wrayton control,
Colinton VOR on test

No reply is expected to such general calls unless individual stations are subsequently called upon to acknowledge receipt.

2.7.3.5   If there is doubt that a message has been correctly received, a repetition of the message shall be requested either in full or in part.

Phrase	Meaning
Say again	Repeat entire message
Say again ... (item)	Repeat specific item
Say again all before ... (the first word satisfactorily received)	
Say again all after ... (the last word satisfactorily received)	
Say again all between ... and ...	

2.7.3.6　When a station is called but is uncertain of the identification of the calling station, the calling station should be requested to repeat its callsign until identification is established.

> Stourton Ground Fastair 345

> Station calling Stourton Ground say again your callsign

2.7.3.7　When an error is made in a transmission the word 'CORRECTION' shall be spoken, the last correct group or phrase repeated and then the correct version transmitted.

> Fastair 345 Wicken 47
> FL 280 Marlow 07
> correction Marlow 57

> Fastair 345 Roger

2.7.3.8　If a correction can best be made by repeating the entire message, the operator shall use the phrase 'CORRECTION I SAY AGAIN' before transmitting the message a second time.

2.7.3.9　Acknowledgements of information should be signified by the use of the receiving stations' callsign or Roger callsign, and not by messages such as: 'callsign-copy the weather' or 'callsign-copy the traffic'.

2.7.4　Transfer of communications

2.7.4.1　An aircraft will normally be advised by the appropriate aeronautical station to change from one radio frequency to another in accordance with agreed procedures.

> Fastair 345 contact
> Wrayton Control 129.1

> Wrayton Control 129.1
> Fastair 345

In the absence of such advice, the aircraft shall notify the aeronautical station before such a change takes place. Aircraft flying in controlled airspace must obtain permission from the controlling authority before changing frequency.

2.7.4.2　An aircraft may be instructed to 'standby' on a frequency when it is intended that the ATSU will initiate further communications, and to monitor a frequency on which information is being broadcast.

Fastair 345 standby for Kennington weather	Fastair 345
Fastair 345 monitor 118.9 for Tower	Monitor 118.9 for Tower Fastair 345

2.7.4.3   If the airspace does not dictate that an aircraft must remain in contact with a specific ATSU and the pilot wishes to freecall another agency he should request, or notify such an intention.

> Westbury G-ABCD request change to Wrayton Information on 125.75

> Wrayton Information G-ABCD changing to Wrayton Centre on 121.5 for Practice Pan

2.7.5   Issue of clearance and read back requirements

2.7.5.1   Provisions governing clearances are contained in the PANS-RAC (ICAO Doc 4444). A clearance may vary in content from a detailed description of the route and levels to be flown to a brief standard instrument departure (SID) according to local procedures.

2.7.5.2   Controllers will pass a clearance slowly and clearly since the pilot needs to write it down; wasteful repetition will thus be avoided. Whenever possible a route clearance should be passed to an aircraft before start up and the aircraft's full callsign will always be used. *Generally controllers will avoid passing a clearance to a pilot engaged in complicated taxying manoeuvres and on no occasion when the pilot is engaged in line up or take-off manoeuvres.*

2.7.5.3   An ATC route clearance is *not* an instruction to take-off or enter an active runway. *The words* **'take-off'** *are used only when an aircraft is cleared for take-off. At all other times the word* **'departure'** *is used.*

2.7.5.4 The stringency of the read back requirement is directly related to the possible seriousness of a misunderstanding in the transmission and receipt of ATC clearance and instructions. *ATC route clearances shall always be read back unless otherwise authorised by the appropriate ATS authority* in which case they shall be acknowledged in a positive manner. Read backs shall always include the aircraft callsign.

Fastair 345 cleared to Kennington via A1, at FL 60, request level change en-route, squawk 5501	Cleared to Kennington via A1, at FL 60, request level change en-route, squawk 5501 Fastair 345
	Fastair 345 correct
Fastair 345 cleared to Kennington via A1, Wicken 3 Delta departure, squawk 5501	Cleared to Kennington via A1, Wicken 3 Delta departure, squawk 5501, Fastair 345
	Fastair 345 correct
G-ABCD after departure cleared to zone boundary via route Echo. Climb to altitude 2000 feet QNH 1008, squawk 6522	After departure cleared to zone boundary via route Echo. Climb to altitude 2000 feet QNH 1008, squawk 6522 G-ABCD
	G-CD correct

2.7.5.5 Pilots of departing aircraft flying in controlled airspace which suffer radio communication failure prior to reaching cruising level should be aware of the procedures to be adopted when the following types of clearance (detailed in UK AIP ENR) are issued:

(a) Request level change en-route.

(b) Climb under radar.

(c) Temporary restriction to climb.

2.7.5.6 The ATS messages listed below are to be read back in full by the pilot. If a readback is not received the pilot will be asked to do so. Similarly, the pilot is expected to request that instructions are repeated or clarified if any are not fully understood.

Taxi Instructions

Level Instructions

Heading Instructions

Speed Instructions

Airways or Route Clearances

Runway-in-Use

Clearance to Enter, Land On, Take-Off On, Backtrack, Cross, or Hold Short of an Active Runway

SSR Operating Instructions

Altimeter Settings

VDF Information

Frequency Changes

Type of Radar Service

G-ABCD cleared to cross A1 at Wicken, maintain FL 70 whilst in controlled airspace. Report entering the airway	Cleared to cross A1 at Wicken , maintain FL 70 in controlled airspace, Wilco. G-ABCD
G-CD hold position	Holding G-CD
G-CD contact Ground 118.05	Ground on 118.05 G-CD
Fastair 345 Squawk 6402	6402 Fastair 345

2.7.5.7 Items which do not appear in the above list may be acknowledged with an abbreviated read back.

> Fastair 345 after the B747
> passing left to right, taxi to
> the holding point runway 23

> After the B747, holding point
> 23, Fastair 345

2.7.5.8   If an aircraft read back of a clearance or instruction is incorrect, the controller shall transmit the word 'NEGATIVE' followed by the correct version.

> G-CD QNH 1003

> QNH 1013 G-CD

> G-CD Negative, QNH 1003

> QNH 1003 G-CD

2.7.5.9   If at any time a pilot receives a clearance or instruction with which he cannot comply, he should advise the controller using the phrase 'UNABLE' (COMPLY) and give the reason(s).

> Fastair 345 Wrayton climb
> FL 280, cross Wicken FL 150
> or above

> Wrayton Fastair 345 unable
> cross Wicken FL 150 due
> weight

2.7.6   Failure to establish or maintain communication

2.7.6.1   *Air to Ground*

(a)   Check the following points:

   (i)   The correct frequency has been selected for the route being flown.

   (ii)   The Aeronautical Station being called is open for watch.

   (iii)   The aircraft is not out of radio range.

   (iv)   Receiver volume correctly set.

(b)   If the previous points are in order it may be that the aircraft equipment is not functioning correctly. Complete the checks of headset and radio installation appropriate to the aircraft.

(c)   If the pilot is still unable to establish communication on any designated aeronautical station frequency, or with any other aircraft, the pilot is to transmit his message twice on the designated frequency preceded by the phrase 'TRANSMITTING BLIND' in case the transmitter is still functioning.

(d)   Where a transmitter failure is suspected, check or change the microphone. Listen out on the designated frequency for instructions. It should be possible to answer questions by use of the carrier wave if the microphone is not functioning (see Chapter 9 para 9.6).

(e)   In the case of a receiver failure transmit reports twice at the scheduled times or positions on the designated frequency preceded by the phrase 'TRANSMITTING BLIND DUE TO RECEIVER FAILURE'.

(f)   An aircraft which is being provided with air traffic control, advisory service or aerodrome flight information is to transmit information regarding the intention of the pilot in command with respect to the continuation of the flight. Specific procedures for the action to be taken by pilots of IFR and Special VFR flights are contained in the appropriate AIP ENR and/or AD sections.

2.7.6.2   *Ground to Air*

After completing checks of ground equipment (most airports have standby and emergency communications equipment) the ground station will request other aeronautical stations and aircraft to attempt to communicate with the aircraft which has failed to maintain contact.

If still unable to establish communication the aeronautical station will transmit messages addressed to the aircraft by blind transmission on the frequency on which the aircraft is believed to be listening.

These will consist of:

(a)   The level, route and EAT (or ETA) to which it is assumed the aircraft is adhering.

(b)   The weather conditions at the destination aerodrome and suitable alternate and, if practicable, the weather conditions in an area or areas suitable for descent through cloud procedure to be effected. (See AIP ENR Section.)

2.7.7   **Test procedures**

2.7.7.1   Test transmissions should take the following form:

(a)   the identification of the aeronautical station being called;

(b)   the aircraft identification;

(c)   the words 'RADIO CHECK';

(d)   the frequency being used.

2.7.7.2   Replies to test transmissions should be as follows:

(a)   the identification of the station calling;

(b)   the identification of the station replying;

(c)   information regarding the readability of the transmission.

2.7.7.3   The readability of a transmission should be classified by the number in the table below, together with any other information regarding the transmission which may be useful to the station making the test.

Readability Scale	Meaning
1	Unreadable
2	Readable now and then
3	Readable but with difficulty
4	Readable
5	Perfectly readable

Borton Tower G-ABCD radio check 118.7	G-ABCD Borton Tower readability 5

or

> G-CD Borton Tower
> readability 3 with a loud
> background whistle

or

> Station calling Borton Tower
> readability 1

2.7.7.4 When it is necessary for a ground station to make test signals, either for the adjustment of a transmitter before making a call or for the adjustment of a receiver, such signals shall not continue for more than 10 seconds. The test should comprise spoken numbers (WUN, TOO, TREE etc) followed by the radio callsign of the station transmitting the test signals.

2.8 PILOTS COMPLAINTS CONCERNING AERONAUTICAL TELECOMMUNICATIONS

Pilots' reports of faults concerning services and facilities in the Aeronautical Mobile, Broadcast and Navigation Services may be recorded on the CAA Form CA 647. The Pilot should ensure that the Briefing Officer, Senior Telecommunications Officer or Senior Controller at the destination or airport of first landing receives full details in order that remedial action can be taken. Reports of local unserviceabilities will be forwarded to the Telecommunications staff if received on RT by the ATSU.

2.9 AIR TRAFFIC SERVICE COMPLAINTS ABOUT AIRCRAFT COMMUNICATIONS

Aircraft radio faults including technical failure, incorrect operating procedures and misuse of specific radio channels may result in the aircraft operator receiving a communication from the CAA detailing the fault condition inviting the operator to explain and/or state what corrective action has been taken.

Chapter 3 – General Phraseology

3.1 INTRODUCTION

3.1.1 The phraseology detailed in this manual has been established for the purpose of ensuring uniformity in RT communications. Obviously, it is not practicable to detail phraseology examples suitable for every situation which may occur. However, if standard phrases are adhered to when composing a message, any possible ambiguity will be reduced to a minimum.

3.1.2 Some abbreviations, which by their common usage have become part of aviation terminology, may be spoken using their constituent letters rather than the spelling alphabet, for example, ILS, QNH, RVR, etc, (see para 1.2).

3.1.3 The following words may be omitted from transmissions provided that no confusion or ambiguity will result:

(a) 'Surface' and 'knots' in relation to surface wind direction and speed.

(b) 'Degrees' in relation to surface wind direction and headings.

(c) 'Visibility', 'cloud' and 'height' in meteorological reports.

(d) 'Millibars' when giving pressure settings of 1000 mbs and above.

(e) 'over', 'roger' and 'out'.

3.1.4 The excessive use of courtesies should be avoided.

3.2 LEVEL INSTRUCTIONS

3.2.1 Only basic level instructions are detailed in this chapter. More comprehensive phrases are contained in subsequent chapters in the context in which they are most commonly used.

3.2.2 The precise phraseology used in the transmission and acknowledgement of climb and descent clearances will vary, depending upon the circumstances, traffic density and nature of the flight operations.

3.2.3 However, care must be taken to ensure that misunderstandings are not generated as a consequence of the phraseology employed during these phases of flight. For example, levels may be reported as altitude, height or flight levels according to the phase of flight and the altimeter setting. Therefore, when passing level messages, the following conventions apply:

(a)   The word 'to' is to be omitted from messages relating to FLIGHT LEVELS.

(b)   All messages relating to an aircraft's *climb or descent* to a HEIGHT or ALTITUDE employ the word 'to' followed immediately by the word HEIGHT or ALTITUDE. Furthermore, the initial message in any such RT exchange will also include the appropriate QFE or QNH.

(c)   The phrase 're-cleared' should not be employed.

G-CD report your level	G-CD maintaining FL 65
	G-CD descend FL 45
	Descend FL 45 G-CD
G-CD report your level	G-CD maintaining altitude 2500 feet regional pressure setting 998 millibars
	G-CD descend to altitude 2000 feet Borton QNH 1000
	Descend to altitude 2000 feet Borton QNH 1000 G-CD
	G-CD descend to altitude 1500 feet
	Desend to altitude 1500 feet G-CD
	G-CD descend to height 1000 feet QFE 997 millibars

32

> Descend to height
> 1000 feet QFE 997 millibars
> G-CD

NOTES: 1 Use of the word 'millibars' for pressures lower than 1000.

2 '1000' millibars is spoken as 'one zero zero zero'.

3.2.3.1 In the following examples the operations of climbing and descending are interchangeable and examples of only one form are given.

G-CD report passing FL 80	Report passing FL 80 G-CD
	G-CD passing FL 80
G-CD maintain altitude 2500 feet	Maintaining altitude 2500 feet G-CD
G-CD climb FL 70	Climb FL 70 G-CD
	G-CD reaching FL70
G-CD request descent	G-CD descend FL 60
	Descend FL 60 G-CD
Fastair 345 after passing North Cross descend FL 80	After passing North Cross descend FL 80 Fastair 345
Fastair 345 stop descent FL 210	Stop descent FL 210 Fastair 345

3.2.3.2 Exceptionally, a *best rate* of climb or descent may be required.

| Fastair 345 expedite descent FL 180 | Expedite descent FL 180 Fastair 345 |

Fastair 345 climb FL 280 expedite until passing FL 180	Climb FL 280 expedite until passing FL 180 Fastair 345
	or
	Fastair 345 unable expedite climb due weight

3.2.3.3 Under exceptional circumstances, if instant descent/climb is required, the word 'immediately' shall be used.

| Fastair 345 descend immediately FL 200 due traffic | Descend immediately FL 200 Fastair 345 |

3.2.3.4 *Pilots are expected to comply with ATC instructions as soon as they are issued.* However, when a climb/descent is left to the discretion of the pilot, the words 'when ready' shall be used; in these circumstances the pilot will report 'leaving' his present level. *Should pilots be instructed to report leaving a level, they should inform ATC that they have left an assigned level only when the aircraft's altimeter indicates that the aircraft has actually departed from that level and is maintaining a positive rate of climb or descent, in accordance with published procedures.*

Fastair 345 when ready climb FL 280	When ready climb FL 280 Fastair 345
	Fastair 345 leaving FL 200 climbing FL 280
	Fastair 345

3.3   POSITION REPORTING

3.3.1   Position reports shall contain the following elements of information:

(a)   Aircraft identification
(b)   Position
(c)   Time
(d)   Level
(e)   Next position and ETA

34

Fastair 345 Wicken 47 FL 280 Marlow 57	Fastair 345

3.3.2 Where adequate flight progress data is available from other sources, such as ground radar, aircraft may be exempted from the requirement to make compulsory position reports.

Fastair 345 next report at Colinton	Wilco Fastair 345

Fastair 345 omit position reports this frequency	Wilco Fastair 345

Fastair 345 resume position reporting	Wilco Fastair 345

3.4   FLIGHT PLANS

3.4.1 A pilot may file a flight plan with an ATSU during flight, although the use of busy RT channels should be avoided; normally the FIS frequency should be used.

Wrayton Control G-ABCD I wish to file an airborne flight plan	G-ABCD Wrayton Control pass your message

3.4.2 The format for an airborne flight plan is as follows:

(a) Aircraft identification and type.
(b) Position and heading.
(c) Level and flight conditions.
(d) Departure aerodrome.
(e) Estimated time at entry point.
(f) Route and point of first intended landing.
(g) True airspeed.
(h) Desired level on airway or advisory route.

3.4.3   During a flight a pilot may elect to cancel an IFR flight plan.

Wrayton Control G-CD cancel my IFR flight plan	G-CD Roger IFR flight plan cancelled at time 47

3.4.4   When a pilot has expressed his intention to cancel an IFR flight plan, the ATSU will pass the pilot any available meteorological information which makes it likely that flight in VMC cannot be maintained.

G-CD IMC reported in the vicinity of Kennington	G-CD Roger remaining IFR

3.5   REPLY TO 'PASS YOUR MESSAGE'

3.5.1   The service that an aircraft requires should be passed in the initial call to the ATSU; when requested by the ATSU to 'pass your message' a suitable reply could contain the following information which, whenever possible, should be given in the following order:

(a)   Aircraft identification and type.
(b)   Point of departure and estimated position.
(c)   Heading.
(d)   Level.
(e)   Intention (next reporting/turning point/destination)
(f)   Type of service required.

Westbury Approach, G-ABCD request Lower Airspace Radar Service	G-ABCD Westbury Approach pass your message
	G-ABCD, T67, from Borton 15 miles south-east of Westbury, heading 350, altitude 2500 feet regional pressure setting 1008, destination Walden, request Radar Information Service

Chapter 4 – Aerodrome Air Traffic Services: Aircraft

4.1 INTRODUCTION

4.1.1 Concise and unambiguous phraseology used at the correct time is vital to the smooth, safe and expeditious running of an aerodrome and associated ATZ. It is not only the means by which instructions and information are passed but it also assists pilots in maintaining an awareness of other traffic in their vicinity, particularly in poor visibility conditions.

4.1.2 Messages will not be transmitted to an aircraft during take-off, the last part of final approach or the landing roll, unless it is necessary for safety reasons, because it will be distracting to the pilot at a time when the cockpit workload is often at its highest.

4.1.3 Local procedures vary from aerodrome to aerodrome and it is impossible to give examples to cover every situation which may arise at the multiplicity of different types of aerodrome. Information in addition to that shown in the examples, eg time checks, etc may be provided as necessary.

4.2 TYPE OF SERVICE

4.2.1 As described in Chapter 2 the type of service provided at an aerodrome falls into one of three categories. In this chapter the examples are confined to those used by air traffic controllers and flight information service officers.

4.2.2 Whilst the RT procedures used by air traffic controllers form the main content of this publication it should be noted that the phraseology used by FISOs is different from that used by controllers. Flight Information Service (FIS) provided at an aerodrome is a service to give information useful for the safe and efficient conduct of flights in the Aerodrome Traffic Zone. From the information received pilots will be able to decide the appropriate course of action to be taken to ensure the safety of flight. Generally, the Flight Information Service Officer (FISO) is not permitted to issue instructions or advice to pilots of his own volition. However, in granting or refusing permission under Rule 35 and 36 of the Rules of the Air, FISOs at aerodromes are permitted to pass instructions to vehicles and personnel operating on the manoeuvring area and information and instructions to aircraft moving on the apron and specific parts of the manoeuvring area. Elsewhere on the manoeuvring area and at all times in the air, information only shall be passed to pilots. Further details on the passing of instructions by FISOs at aerodromes are contained in CAP 410 Part B Aerodromes.

4.2.3   FIS is available at aerodromes during the hours of operation indicated in the UK AIP. The service is easily identifiable by the callsign suffix 'INFORMATION'.

4.2.4   The Flight Information Service Officer (FISO) at an aerodrome is responsible for:

(a)   Issuing information to aircraft flying in the Aerodrome Traffic Zone to assist pilots in preventing collisions.

(b)   Issuing instructions and information to aircraft on the manoeuvring area to assist pilots in preventing collisions between aircraft and vehicles/obstructions on the manoeuvring area or between aircraft moving on the apron.

(c)   Issuing instructions to vehicles and persons on the manoeuvring area.

(d)   Informing aircraft of essential aerodrome information (ie the state of the aerodrome and its facilities).

(e)   Alerting the safety services.

(f)   Initiating overdue action.

4.2.5   FISOs are also permitted to pass messages on behalf of other agencies and instructions from the aerodrome operator. If they do so, they will include the name of the agency so that pilots will be aware that the message comes from a legitimate source, eg 'Wrayton Control clears you to join ...'.

4.3   DEPARTURE INFORMATION AND ENGINE STARTING PROCEDURES

4.3.1   Where no ATIS is provided the pilot may ask for current aerodrome information before requesting start up.

Stourton Ground Fastair 345, request departure information	Fastair 345 Stourton Ground departure runway 32 wind 290 4, QNH 1008, temperature –2, dewpoint –3, RVR 550 metres

Runway 32, QNH 1008, will call for start up Fastair 345

4.3.2   Requests to start engines are normally made to facilitate ATC planning and to avoid excessive fuel wastage by aircraft delayed on the ground. At certain aerodromes, along with the request, the pilot will state the location of the aircraft and acknowledge receipt of the departure ATIS broadcast identifying letter together with the QNH.

Stourton Ground Fastair 345, stand 24 information Bravo, QNH 1022 request start up	Fastair 345 Stourton Ground start up at time 35

4.3.3   When there will be a delay to the departure of the aircraft the controller will normally indicate a time to start up or expect to start up.

Stourton Ground Fastair 345 information Charlie QNH 1022, request start up	Fastair 345 Stourton Ground start up approved, temperature –2

or

Fastair 345 Stourton Ground expect start up at time 35

or

Fastair 345 Stourton Ground expect departure at time 49 start up when ready, temperature –2

4.4   PUSHBACK AND POWERBACK

4.4.1   At many aerodromes at which large aircraft operate, the aircraft are parked nose-in to the terminal in order to save parking space. Aircraft have to be pushed backwards by tugs before they can taxi for departure. Some aircraft also have the capability to reverse from a nose-in position to the terminal under their own power. This procedure is known as powerback. Requests for pushback or powerback are made to ATC depending on the local procedures.

> Fastair 345 stand 27 request pushback/powerback

> Fastair 345 pushback/ powerback approved

> or

> Fastair 345 negative. Expect one minute delay due B747 taxying behind

4.5   TAXI INSTRUCTIONS

4.5.1   Taxi instructions issued by a controller will always contain a clearance limit, which is the point at which the aircraft must stop unless further permission to proceed is given. For departing aircraft the clearance limit will normally be the holding point of the runway in use, but it may be any other position on the aerodrome depending on the prevailing traffic.

> Borton Tower G-ABCD T67 by the south side hangars request taxi for VFR flight to Walden

> G-CD taxi to holding point runway 24 via taxiway Charlie QNH 967 millibars

> Taxi to holding point runway 24 via taxiway Charlie QNH 967 millibars G-CD

> G-CD request surface wind

> G-CD surface wind 220 6

> G-CD request runway 14

> G-CD follow the Seneca coming from your left taxi to holding point runway 14

Following the Seneca, taxi to holding point runway 14. G-CD

Borton Tower G-ABCD T67 at the fuel station VFR to Walden request taxi

G-CD runway 06 QNH 1008 taxi to holding point runway 14 via taxiway Alpha

QNH 1008 G-CD request taxiway Bravo, and backtrack runway 24

G-CD taxi holding point runway 24 via taxiway Bravo

Taxi holding point runway 24 via taxiway Bravo G-CD

Borton Tower G-ABCD at the fuel station request taxi to flying club

G-CD taxi to holding point runway 24 via Charlie

Taxi holding point runway 24 via Charlie G-CD

G-CD holding point runway 24 request cross

G-CD negative. I will call you

Holding G-CD

G-CD taxi to the flying club, cross runway 24 at the threshold report vacated

> Taxi to the flying club cross
> runway 24 at the threshold
> will report vacated G-CD

> G-CD runway vacated

> G-CD

Note: Report vacated may be omitted when aerodrome control has continuous sight of the aircraft crossing.

4.5.2   Where an ATIS broadcast is established the controller does not need to pass departure information to the pilot when giving taxi instructions. He will, however, check that the aircraft is in possession of the latest QNH.

> Fastair 345 information Bravo,
> QNH 1020 request taxi

> Fastair 345, QNH 1021, after
> the B747 passing left to right
> taxi to holding point runway
> 28

> QNH 1021, after B747
> holding point runway 28
> Fastair 345

4.6   PRE-DEPARTURE MANOEUVRING

4.6.1   Meticulous care has been taken to ensure that the phraseology which is to be employed during the pre-departure manoeuvres cannot be interpreted as a take-off clearance. This is to avoid the serious consequences that could result if there is any misunderstanding in the granting or acknowledgement of take-off clearances.

4.6.2   At busy aerodromes with a separate ground and tower function, aircraft are usually transferred to the tower frequency at or approaching the holding point.

Fastair 345 contact Tower 118.9	Tower 118.9 Fastair 345

4.6.3 Many types of aircraft carry out engine checks prior to departure and are not always ready for take-off when they reach the holding point.

G-CD report when ready for departure	Wilco G-CD

G-CD ready for departure	G-CD line up

Line up G-CD

4.7 TAKE-OFF PROCEDURES

4.7.1 Except in cases of emergency, messages will not be transmitted to an aircraft in the process of taking off or in the final stages of an approach and landing.

Controllers will use the following phraseology for take off.

G-CD cleared take-off	Cleared take-off G-CD

Note: The surface wind will be passed if there is a significant difference to that already passed.

FISOs will use different phraseology to indicate that there is nothing to prevent an aircraft taking off:

Buckby Information G-BJRD ready for departure	G-RD Buckby Information take-off at your discretion .. surface wind 280 ..... (traffic information)

4.7.2 For traffic reasons a controller may consider it necessary for an aircraft to take off without any delay. Therefore, when given the instruction 'cleared for immediate take-off', the pilot is expected to act as follows:

(a)   At the holding point: taxi immediately on to the runway and commence take-off without stopping the aircraft.

(b)   If already lined up on the runway: take-off without delay.

Fastair 345 cleared immediate take-off	Cleared immediate take-off Fastair 345

4.7.3   For reason of expedition a controller may wish to line-up an aircraft for departure before conditions allow take-off.

Fastair 345 line-up and wait – vehicle crossing upwind end of runway	Line-up and wait Fastair 345
Fastair 345 cleared take-off	Cleared take-off Fastair 345

4.7.4   In poor visibility the controller may state the runway and request the pilot to report when airborne.

Fastair cleared take-off runway 28 report airborne	Cleared take-off runway 28. Wilco. Fastair 345
	Fastair 345 airborne
	Fastair 345 contact Radar 121.75
	Radar 121.75 Fastair 345

4.7.5   Conditional phrases will not be used for movements affecting the active runway(s), except when the aircraft or vehicles concerned are seen by the controller and pilot. Conditional clearances are to relate to one movement only and, in the case of landing traffic, this must be the first aircraft on approach. A conditional instruction shall be given as follows:

(a)   callsign;

(b)   the condition;

(c)   identification of subject of the condition;

(d)   the instruction.

Fastair 345 after the landing DC9, line up	After the landing DC9 line up Fastair 345

4.7.6   When several runways are in use and/or there is any possibility that the pilot may be confused as to which one to use, the runway number will be stated.

Fastair 345 cleared take-off runway 09 left	Cleared take-off runway 09 left Fastair 345

4.7.7   Local departure instructions may be given with the take-off clearance. Such instructions are normally given to ensure separation between aircraft operating in the vicinity of the aerodrome.

Fastair 345 after departure climb straight ahead to altitude 2500 feet before turning right. Cleared take-off	After departure climb straight ahead to altitude 2500 feet before turning right. Cleared take-off Fastair 345

G-CD after departure request right turn	G-CD right turn approved cleared take-off

	Right turn approved cleared take-off G-CD

4.7.8   Due to unexpected traffic developments or a departing aircraft taking longer to take-off than anticipated, it is occasionally necessary to rescind the take-off clearance or quickly free the runway for landing traffic.

Fastair 345 take-off immediately or vacate runway	Taking-off Fastair 345
Fastair 345 take-off immediately or hold short of runway	Holding short Fastair 345

4.7.9   When an aircraft is about to take-off or has commenced the take-off roll, and it is necessary that the aircraft should abandon take-off, the aircraft will be instructed to cancel take-off or stop immediately; these instructions will be repeated.

G-CD hold position, cancel I say again cancel take-off, acknowledge	Holding G-CD
Fastair 345 stop immediately I say again Fastair 345 stop immediately, acknowledge	Stopping Fastair 345

4.7.10   When a pilot abandons take-off he should, as soon as practicable, inform the tower that he is doing so. Likewise, as soon as practicable, he should inform the tower of the reasons for abandoning take-off if applicable, and request further manoeuvring instructions.

Fastair 345 stopping	Fastair 345
	Fastair 345 request backtrack for another departure
	Fastair 345 backtrack approved

4.8   AERODROME TRAFFIC CIRCUIT

4.8.1

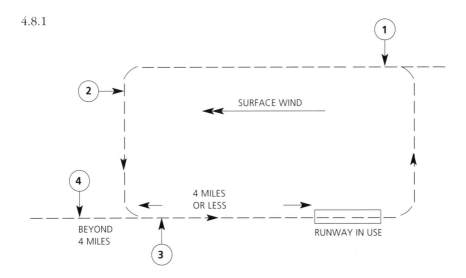

Typical Left-hand Circuit

Position 1   Aircraft reports on downwind leg when abeam upwind end of runway.

Position 2   Base leg report (if required).

Position 3   'Final' report. Clearance to land issued here.

Position 4   'Long final' report (between 8 and 4 miles) when aircraft is on a straight in approach.

Note: For light aircraft operations, circuit dimensions may be reduced but the relative RT reporting points are maintained.

Figure 1 Critical positions in the traffic circuit

4.8.2   Requests for circuit-joining instructions should be made in sufficient time for a planned entry into the circuit taking other traffic into account. Where ATIS is established, receipt of the broadcast should be acknowledged in the initial call to an aerodrome. When the traffic circuit is a right-hand pattern it shall be specified. A left-hand pattern *need not* be specified although it is *essential* to do so when the circuit direction is variable.

Walden Tower G-ABCD T67 10 miles south altitude 2500 feet regional pressure setting 1008 request joining instructions	G-CD join righthand downwind runway 27 height 1000 feet QFE 1006

	Join righthand downwind runway 27 height 1000 feet QFE 1006 G-CD

4.8.3 In some circumstances, an aircraft may be instructed to complete a standard overhead join which comprises the following:

(a) Overfly at 2000 ft above Aerodrome Elevation.

(b) If not already known, determine the circuit direction from the signals square, other traffic or windsock.

(c) Descend on the 'dead side' to circuit height ('G-CD deadside descending').

(d) Join the circuit by crossing the upwind end of the runway at circuit height.

(e) Position downwind.

Note: Aerodromes with overhead joins at variance to the above standard procedure will notify such differences.

4.8.4 Depending on prevailing traffic conditions and the direction from which an aircraft is arriving, it may be possible to make a straight-in approach.

Walden Tower G-ABCD T67 10 miles south altitude 2500 feet regional pressure setting 1008 request straight-in approach runway 34	G-CD cleared straight in approach runway 34 surface wind 260 degrees 5 knots QFE 1006 report final

	Cleared straight in approach runway 34 QFE 1006. Wilco. G-CD

4.8.5 The pilot having joined the traffic circuit makes routine reports as required by local procedures.

G-CD downwind	G-CD number 2 follow the Cherokee on base
	Number 2, contact with the Cherokee G-CD
G-CD base	G-CD
G-CD final	G-CD cleared to land runway 34 surface wind 270 7
	Cleared to land runway 34 G-CD

4.8.6 It may be necessary in order to co-ordinate traffic in the circuit to issue delaying or expediting instructions.

G-CD extend downwind number 2 to a Cherokee 4 miles final	Extend downwind, number 2 G-CD
G-CD delaying action. Orbit right report again on base	Orbit right, Wilco G-CD

4.8.7 In order to save taxying time when flying training in the traffic circuit pilots may wish to carry out a 'touch and go', ie the aircraft lands, continues rolling and takes-off, without stopping.

G-CD downwind touch and go	G-CD Roger

> G-CD final

> G-CD cleared touch and go
> runway 34 surface wind calm

> Cleared touch and go
> runway 34 G-CD

or

> G-CD unable to approve due
> traffic make full stop landing
> cleared to land runway 34
> surface wind calm

> Cleared to land runway 34
> G-CD

4.8.8   It is helpful for circuit management purposes if a controller is informed when an aircraft which has been engaged in multiple approaches is on his last circuit.

> G-CD downwind last landing   G-CD Roger

4.9   FINAL APPROACH AND LANDING

4.9.1   A 'final' report is made when an aircraft turns onto final approach. If the turn on is made at a distance greater than 4 nm from touchdown a 'long final' report is made. The landing/touch and go/low approach clearance will include the runway designation.

> G-CD final   G-CD cleared to land
>   runway 34 surface wind
>   270 7

>   Cleared to land runway 34
>   G-CD

50

| Fastair 345 long final | Fastair 345 report final surface wind 260 18 |

Wilco Fastair 345

Fastair 345 final

Fastair 345 cleared to land runway 28 surface wind 270 20

Cleared to land runway 28 Fastair 345

Note: *Where established an 'outer marker' instead of a 'final' report may be made.*

4.9.2   The runway may be obstructed when the aircraft makes its 'final' report at 4 nm or less from touchdown but is expected to be available in good time for the aircraft to make a safe landing. On these occasions the controller will delay landing clearance.

| G-CD final | G-CD Continue approach surface wind 270 5 |

Continue approach G-CD

The controller may or may not explain why the landing clearance has been delayed but the instruction to 'continue' IS NOT an invitation to land and the pilot must wait for landing clearance or initiate a missed approach (see para 4.10.3).

4.9.3   A landing aircraft may be permitted to touch down before a preceding landing aircraft which has landed is clear of the runway provided that:

(a)   the runway is long enough to allow safe separation between the two aircraft and there is no evidence to indicate that braking may be adversely affected;

(b)   it is during daylight hours;

(c)   the controller is satisfied that the landing aircraft will be able to see the preceding aircraft which has landed, clearly and continuously, until it is clear of the runway; and

(d)   the pilot of the following aircraft is warned. (Responsibility for ensuring adequate separation rests with the pilot of the following aircraft.)

Fastair 345, land after the B737, runway 28, surface wind calm	Land after the B737 Fastair 345

4.9.4   A pilot may request to fly past the control tower or other observation point for the purpose of visual inspection from the ground.

Fastair 345 request low pass unsafe left gear indication	Fastair 345 cleared low pass runway 28 surface wind 270 10 not below 500 feet QFE 1006 report final
	Cleared low pass runway 28 not below 500 feet QFE 1006 Wilco Fastair 345

4.9.5   If the low pass is made for the purpose of observing the undercarriage, one of the following replies could be used to describe its condition but these examples are not exhaustive:

(a)   landing gear appears down;

(b)   right (or left, or nose) wheel appears up (or down);

(c)   wheels appear up;

(d)   right (or left, or nose) wheel does not appear up (or down).

4.9.6   For training purposes, a pilot may request permission to make an approach along, or parallel to the runway, without landing.

> Fastair 345 request low approach for training

> Fastair 345 cleared low approach runway 28 surface wind 270 6 not below 400 feet above threshold elevation report final

> Cleared low approach runway 28 not below 400 feet above threshold elevation Wilco Fastair 345

4.9.7   FISOs will use different phraseology to indicate that there is nothing to prevent an aircraft from landing.

> Buckby Information G-BJRD final runway 24

> G-BJRD Buckby Information land at your discretion surface wind 260 6

> G-BJRD

4.9.8   Alternatively, if the runway is obstructed, or there are other aircraft ahead on final, FISOs will use:

> G-BJRD final runway 24

> G-BJRD Buckby Information, the runway is obstructed with a PA28

or

> G-BJRD Buckby Information, 2 aircraft ahead on final

> G-BJRD

4.10 GO AROUND

4.10.1 Instructions to carry out a missed approach may be given to avert an unsafe situation. When a missed approach is initiated cockpit workload is inevitably high. Any transmissions to aircraft going around will be brief and kept to a minimum.

> Fastair 345 go around
> I say again go around
> acknowledge

> Going around Fastair 345

4.10.2 An aircraft on an instrument approach is to carry out the published missed approach procedure and an aircraft operating VFR is to continue into the normal traffic circuit unless instructions are issued to the contrary.

4.10.3 In the event of missed approach being initiated by the pilot the phrase 'going around' shall be used.

> G-CD going around

> G-CD Roger

4.10.4 At military aerodromes 'GO AROUND' is also employed to instruct an aircraft to fly another circuit. Unless otherwise instructed, circuit height should be maintained (or regained) and a 'Deadside' call made before turning Crosswind to report Downwind.

4.11 AFTER LANDING

4.11.1 Unless absolutely necessary, controllers will not give taxi instructions to pilots until the landing roll is complete. Unless otherwise advised pilots should remain on tower frequency until the runway is vacated.

> Fastair 345 vacate left

> Vacate left Fastair 345

> Fastair 345 take next right
> when vacated contact
> Ground 118.35

> Next right when vacated
> Ground 118.35 Fastair 345

> Kennington Ground
> Fastair 345 runway vacated

> Fastair 345 Kennington
> Ground taxi to stand 27 via
> taxiway Alpha

> Stand 27 via taxiway Alpha
> Fastair 345

> G-CD taxi to the end report
> runway vacated

> Taxi to the end, Wilco G-CD

> G-CD runway vacated

> G-CD taxi to the flying club

> Taxi to the flying club G-CD

4.12 ESSENTIAL AERODROME INFORMATION

4.12.1 Essential Aerodrome Information is information regarding the manoeuvring area and its associated facilities which is necessary to ensure the safe operation of aircraft. Essential Aerodrome Information is passed to aircraft whenever possible prior to start-up or taxi and prior to the commencement of final approach.

> Fastair 345 caution
> construction work at the
> end of Stand 37

> ... caution work in progress
> ahead north side of taxiway
> Alpha

... caution centre line taxiway lighting unserviceable

... caution PAPIs runway 27 unserviceable

... caution large flock of birds north of runway 27 near centre taxiway

... message from aerodrome authority, fire and rescue services reduced. The aerodrome can only accept aircraft up to and including category (number)

4.13 EXAMPLES OF FISO PHRASEOLOGY (AERODROMES)

	Phraseology
Aircraft ready to taxi	..... (callsign) taxi holding point runway ..... left/right hand circuit, QFE/QNH ..... surface wind
When aircraft or vehicles request permission to cross a runway	..... (callsign) cross runway ..... report vacated OR ..... (callsign) hold position
Aircraft reports ready for departure	..... (callsign) hold position holding ..... (callsign)* OR ..... (callsign) there is a ..... (aircraft type) landing to vacate and a ..... (aircraft type) on a 2 mile final. report lining up lining up ..... (callsign) OR roger holding position ..... (callsign)* OR ..... (callsign) surface wind ..... take off at your discretion taking off ..... (callsign)*
When airborne	..... (aircraft callsign) roger, report ..... (downwind or position)
Aircraft wishes to transit the ATZ	..... (aircraft callsign) ..... (traffic and aerodrome information), **report** entering/ overhead/leaving.
Aircraft wishes to enter the ATZ for landing	..... (aircraft callsign) runway ..... left/right hand circuit, QFE/QNH ..... surface wind ..... (traffic information and essential aerodrome information as appropriate).
Aircraft reports joining the circuit	..... (aircraft callsign) roger, (traffic information) **report** downwind/base leg/final.
Aircraft reports final *(If number one and runway clear)* *(If aircraft has traffic ahead on final)* *(If the runway is occupied)*	..... (callsign) land/touch and go at your discretion, surface wind ..... landing /touch and go ..... (callsign) OR going around ..... (callsign)* OR ..... (callsign) roger, (number) aircraft ahead on final ..... (callsign) roger* OR ..... (callsign) the runway is occupied with (traffic details) ..... (callsign) roger OR ..... (callsign) going around.*
Aircraft reports landed and/or runway vacated	..... (callsign) roger, (taxi information)

* Phraseology by pilot.

Notes: 1 Full details are contained within CAP 410 Part B.

2 Pilots are required to report entering and leaving ATZ. FISOs may request pilots to *report* at positions in the circuit for the provision of traffic information

3 Some examples are included at Chapter 12 para 12.3.12.

4.14 EXAMPLES OF AIR–GROUND OPERATORS PHRASEOLOGY

Event	*Response*
A/C ready to taxi	..... (aircraft callsign) runway ..... circuit direction ..... QFE/QNH ..... millibars
A/C wishes to cross a runway	..... (aircraft callsign) traffic information eg I have no known traffic; OR ..... (aircraft callsign) after ..... has landed I have no known traffic
A/C ready to take off	..... (aircraft callsign) no known traffic or Traffic Information Surface wind .....
A/C reports airborne	..... (aircraft callsign) roger
A/C reports entering ATZ or asks for traffic information	..... (aircraft callsign) traffic information ..... (aircraft callsign) aerodrome information
A/C intends to land	..... (aircraft callsign) runway ..... Surface wind ..... QFE/QNH ..... millibars Traffic information
A/C reports joining circuit downwind, base leg or final	..... (aircraft callsign) roger (plus when applicable latest aerodrome and traffic information)
A/C reports landed and/or runway vacated	..... (aircraft callsign) any appropriate aerodrome information

Notes: 1   Full details are contained within CAP 452.

2   Air–ground operators should not use the expression 'at your discretion' as this is associated with the service provided by FISOs.

4.14.1

Seaton Radio G-ABCD request radio check 123.0 and taxi information

G-ABCD Seaton Radio readability 5 runway 23 left hand circuit QFE/QNH 1022

Seaton Radio, G-ABCD readability 5 also, taxiing for runway 23 left hand 1022

G-CD Seaton roger

G-CD ready for departure	G-CD roger. No known traffic, surface wind 230 degrees 10 knots
Roger taking off G-CD	or
	G-CD there is a Cherokee on 2 mile final, surface wind 230 degrees 10 knot
Roger taking off G-CD	

or

Roger holding position G-CD	

once Cherokee has landed and vacated

G-CD lining-up and taking off	G-CD roger surface wind 230 degrees 10 knots
G-CD leaving the circuit to the west. Will report when re-joining	G-CD roger two other aircraft known to be operating VFR to the west
	Roger G-CD
Seaton Radio this is G-BCDA	G-BCDA Seaton Radio pass your message

Seaton G-BCDA is a PA28 from Westbury overhead Marlow heading 180 altitude 1800 feet on QNH 1021 estimating overhead Seaton at 1015 en route Millom, request traffic information

G-DA Seaton roger, runway 23 is active left hand with one Cessna downwind. Seaton QNH 1022.

QNH 1022 I will report overhead G-DA

G-DA overhead at 15 will report leaving the frequency

G-DA roger

G-DA is now clear of your ATZ changing to en route frequency

G-DA roger

Seaton Radio G-ABCD 6 miles west of the airfield request airfield information

G-CD Seaton runway 23 left hand, QFE 1021. There is one Cessna on left base

Roger. Runway 23 left hand, QFE 1021 G-CD

G-CD overhead descending deadside for runway 23

G-CD roger no known traffic

or

G-CD downwind

G-CD roger no known traffic

G-CD final

G-CD roger surface wind 220/15. There is one Cessna lining up to depart

G-CD roger

G-CD vacating to the left and returning to the club

G-CD roger

G-CD ready to cross runway 15

G-CD roger no known traffic

Roger G-CD

Chapter 5 – Aerodrome Air Traffic Services: Vehicles

5.1 INTRODUCTION

5.1.1 The expeditious movement of vehicles plays an essential supporting role in the operation of an aerodrome. Whenever possible the areas in which vehicles and aircraft operate are segregated. However, there are many occasions when vehicles need to move on the manoeuvring area either for maintenance purposes or in direct support of aircraft operations.

5.1.2 Procedures governing the movement of vehicles vary widely from aerodrome to aerodrome, but certain factors to be taken into account when driving on an aerodrome are common to all:

(a) in general, aircraft are by no means as manoeuvrable as ground vehicles;

(b) the visibility from an aircraft cockpit for ground movement purposes is often restricted compared with a vehicle.

Therefore when vehicles are operating in close proximity to aircraft, drivers should be extremely vigilant and comply with Rule 36/37 of the Rules of the Air 1996 and, if applicable, ATC instructions.

5.1.3 Correct RT operating technique must be observed by all users. For all vehicles on the movement area, it is important that a continuous listening watch is maintained, not only in case of further instructions or information from the tower, but also so that drivers can be aware of the movements, and intended movements, of other traffic thereby reducing the risk of confliction.

5.2 MOVEMENT INSTRUCTIONS

5.2.1 Drivers on first call should identify themselves by their vehicle call sign, state their position and intended destination (and possibly required route).

Ground Works 21 stand 27 request proceed to work in progress taxiway hotel	Works 21 proceed to taxiway Hotel via Kilo and Alpha
	Taxiway Hotel via Kilo and Alpha Works 21

63

5.2.2   If the controller is too busy he will reply 'standby'. This means that the driver should wait until the controller calls back. The driver shall *not* proceed until permission is given.

5.2.3   When there is conflicting traffic the controller may reply 'hold position'. This means that the driver shall not proceed until the controller calls back with permission. All other replies should contain a clearly defined point to which the driver may proceed; this may or may not be the intended destination. If it is not the intended destination drivers must stop at this point and further permission shall be requested.

Ground Tels 5 at Charlie 8
request proceed to hangar 3

Tels 5 proceed to holding
point runway 14 at Charlie 1

Proceeding to holding point
runway 14 at Charlie 1 Tels 5

Note: the vehicle has only been cleared as far as the holding point to await runway crossing clearance and permission to proceed to hangar 3.

5.2.4   Permission to proceed on the apron may include instructions to ensure safe operations.

Ground Tug 5 stand 21
request proceed to gate 26

Tug 5 after the Fastair
BAe 146 on your right has
passed, proceed to stand 26,
caution jet blast

After the BAe 146 has passed
proceed stand 26, Tug 5

5.3   CROSSING RUNWAYS

5.3.1   Drivers should note carefully the position to which they may proceed, particularly where the intended route involves crossing a runway. Some aerodromes may have procedures that will allow vehicles to proceed to a holding point on the movement area and then request runway crossing instructions. Under no circumstances shall a driver cross a runway unless *positive permission has been given and acknowledged.* A runway vacated report should not be made until the vehicle (and tow) is clear of the designated runway area.

Ground Works 21 by the control tower request proceed to maintenance base	Works 21 proceed to holding point runway 32 via Alpha and Bravo
	Proceeding to holding point runway 32 via Alpha and Bravo Works 21
	Works 21 holding point runway 32 request cross
	Works 21 hold position
	Holding Works 21
Works 21 cross runway 32 proceed to maintenance base via Foxtrot	Crossing runway 32 proceeding to maintenance base via Foxtrot Works 21

5.3.2   If a vehicle is operating on the runway, it will be instructed to vacate the runway when it is expected that an aircraft will be landing or taking off.

| Works 21 vacate runway 27 take next right, report vacated | Vacate next right, Wilco Works 21 |

| | Works 21 runway 27 vacated |

| | Works 21 |

5.3.3 When a vehicle is moving on the movement area it may be necessary to inform the vehicle of a potentially dangerous situation and to tell it to stop.

| Works 21 stop immediately aircraft crossing ahead | Stopping Works 21 |

5.4 VEHICLES TOWING AIRCRAFT

5.4.1 Drivers of vehicles required to tow aircraft should not assume that the receiving station is aware that an aircraft is to be towed. The performance and manoeuvrability of ground vehicles is obviously considerably reduced when towing aircraft and this is taken into account when instructions to such vehicles are issued. Therefore, in order to avoid any confusion, and as an aid to identification, drivers should state the type, and where applicable the operator, of the aircraft to be towed in the first call.

| Ground tug 9 request tow Fastair BAe 146 from stand 25 to maintenance hangar 3 | Tug 9, tow approved from stand 25 to maintenance hangar 3 via Echo |

| | Tow to maintenance hangar 3 via Echo Tug 9 |

Chapter 6 – General Radar Phraseology

6.1 INTRODUCTION

6.1.1 This chapter contains general radar phraseology which is commonly used in communications between aircraft and all types of radar unit. Phraseology which is more applicable to approach radar control or area control is to be found in Chapter 7 and 8 as appropriate.

6.1.2 The phrase 'under radar control' shall only be used when a radar control service is being provided. Normally however, the callsign suffix used by the radar unit is sufficient to indicate its function.

6.1.3 In a radar environment heading information given by the pilot and heading instructions given by controllers are normally in degrees magnetic.

6.2 RADAR IDENTIFICATION AND VECTORING

6.2.1 An aircraft must be identified before it can be provided with a radar service. However, the act of identifying aircraft is not a service in itself and pilots should *not* assume that they are receiving a radar service, particularly when they are flying outside controlled airspace.

G-CD report heading	G-CD heading 350
	G-CD for identification turn left heading 320
Left heading 320 G-CD	
	G-CD identified 18 miles north-west of Borton, Radar Advisory
Radar Advisory G-CD	

or

6.2.2   When a controller has identified an aircraft he will inform the pilot, according to the circumstances, of the following:

(a)   that the aircraft is identified, and

(b)   of the position of the aircraft.

The occasions when the above information will be passed can be summarised as follows:

Method of Identification	Aircraft flying inside controlled airspace		Aircraft flying outside controlled airspace	
	Inform Identified	Pass Position	Inform Identified	Pass Position
SSR	No	No	Yes	Yes
Turn	Yes	Yes	Yes	Yes
Departing aircraft	No	No	Yes	No
Position Report	No	No	Yes	No

6.2.3   The pilot will be warned if identification is lost, or about to be lost, and appropriate instructions given.

> G-CD radar service terminated due radar failure. Resume own navigation. Flight Information available from Wrayton on 125.75

> Changing to Wrayton 125.75 G-CD

> G-CD will shortly be leaving radar cover, radar service terminated. Flight Information available from Wrayton on 125.75

> G-CD changing to Wrayton 125.75

> G-CD

6.3   SECONDARY SURVEILLANCE RADAR

6.3.1   The following phrases are instructions which may be given by controllers to pilots regarding the operation of SSR transponders. The phrases used by controllers are given together with their meanings; assignment of a code *does not* constitute the provision of a radar service.

Phrase	*Meaning*
Squawk (code)	Set the mode and code as instructed
Confirm squawk	Confirm the mode and code set on the transponder
Recycle (mode) (code)	Reselect assignment mode and code

Phrase	Meaning
Squawk Ident	Operate the special position identification feature
Squawk Mayday	Select Emergency
Squawk Standby	Select the standby feature
Squawk Charlie	Select altitude reporting feature
Check altimeter setting and report your level	Check pressure setting and report your level
Stop squawk Charlie	Deselect altitude reporting
Stop squawk Charlie, Wrong indication	Stop altitude report, incorrect level readout
*Verify your level	Check and confirm your level

*Used to verify the accuracy of the Mode C derived level information displayed to the controller.

6.3.2   The pilot must respond to SSR instructions, reading back specific settings.

Fastair 345 squawk 6411	6411 Fastair 345
Fastair 345 squawk ident	Squawk ident, Fastair 345
Fastair 345 squawk 6411 and ident	6411 and ident, Fastair 345
Fastair 345 confirm squawk	Alpha 6411 Fastair 345
Fastair 345 recycle 6411	Recycling 6411 Fastair 345

Fastair 345 check altimeter setting	1013 set Fastair 345
Fastair 345 confirm transponder operating	Fastair 345 negative, transponder unserviceable

6.4 RADAR SERVICE

6.4.1 Where it is not self-evident pilots will normally be informed by the controller when they are under radar control, advisory or information service.

Fastair 345 under Radar Control	Radar Control Fastair 345
G-CD Radar Advisory	Radar Advisory G-CD
G-CD Radar Information	Radar Information G-CD
Fastair 345 radar service terminated	Fastair 345

6.5 RADAR VECTORING

6.5.1 Aircraft may be given specific vectors to fly in order to establish separation. Pilots may be informed of the reasons for radar vectoring.

Fastair 345 delaying action. Turn left heading 050	Left heading 050 Fastair 345

6.5.2 It may be necessary for a controller to know the heading of an aircraft as separation can often be established by instructing an aircraft to continue on its existing heading.

Fastair 345 continue present heading	Continue heading Fastair 345
Fastair 345 report heading	Fastair 345 heading 050
Fastair 345 continue present heading and report that heading	Continue heading 050 Fastair 345
Fastair 345 continue heading 050	Continue heading 050 Fastair 345

6.5.3   A controller may not know the aircraft's heading but does require the aircraft to fly a particular heading.

G-CD fly heading 275	Roger, turning left heading 275, G-CD
	or
	Roger, turning right 20 degrees heading 275, G-CD

6.5.4   When vectoring is complete, pilots will be instructed to resume their own navigation, given position information and appropriate instructions as necessary.

Fastair 345 resume own navigation for Wicken, magnetic track 070 distance 27 miles	Wilco Fastair 345
G-CD resume own navigation for Walden position is 15 miles southeast of Westbury	Wilco G-CD

72

6.5.5   Occasionally an aircraft may be instructed to make a complete turn (known as an orbit or a 360 degree turn), for delaying purposes or to achieve a required spacing behind preceding traffic.

G-CD delaying action, orbit left for sequencing	Orbit left G-CD
Fastair 345 delaying action. Make a 360 degree turn left	360 turn left Fastair 345

6.6   TRAFFIC INFORMATION AND TRAFFIC AVOIDANCE

6.6.1   Whenever practicable, information regarding traffic on a possible conflicting path should be given in the following form:

(a)   relative bearing of the conflicting traffic in terms of the 12 hour clock; or, if the aircraft under service is established in a turn, the relative position of the conflicting traffic in relation to cardinal points ie northwest, south etc;

(b)   distance from the conflicting traffic;

(c)   direction of flight of the conflicting traffic; and

(d)   relative speed of the conflicting traffic or the type of aircraft and level if this is known.

6.6.2   Relative movement should be described by using one of the following terms as applicable:

'closing, converging, parallel, same direction, opposite direction diverging, overtaking, crossing left to right, crossing right to left; (if level is known) – 1000 feet above/below.'

6.6.3   The controller will inform the pilot when the conflict no longer exists.

G-CD unknown traffic
10 o'clock 6 miles crossing
left to right height unknown
fast moving. If not sighted
turn left heading 270

Left heading 270 G-CD

G-CD clear of traffic resume
own navigation direct
Walden magnetic track 350
distance 13 miles

Wilco G-CD

6.6.4   Avoiding action to be taken by the pilot is given when the controller
considers that an imminent risk of collision will exist if action is not
taken immediately.

G-CD avoiding action, turn
left immediately heading 270
traffic at 10 o'clock 5 miles
crossing left to right
indicating slightly above fast
moving

Left heading 270 G-CD

6.7   ACAS/TCAS

6.7.1   ACAS/TCAS equipment reacts to transponders of other aircraft in the
vicinity to determine whether or not there is a potential confliction. The
warning (Traffic Advisory (TA)), based on the time to an assumed
collision enables the pilot to identify the conflicting traffic, and if
necessary, take avoiding action (Resolution Advisory (RA)). In the UK,
this equipment is mainly referred to as 'TCAS', however, the use of
'ACAS' is an acceptable alternative in phraseology terms.

6.7.2   Pilots should report TCAS manoeuvres.

Fastair 345 TCAS climb/
descent

Fastair 345 Roger

> Fastair 345 TCAS clear of
> conflict, returning to
> (assigned clearance)

> Fastair 345 Roger

> (Controllers may issue a revised
> clearance at this point.)

6.7.3   The pilot should report a TCAS manoeuvre even if it was not possible to notify the Controller that an RA had occurred.

> Fastair 345 TCAS climb/
> descent, clear of conflict,
> (assigned clearance) resumed

> Fastair 345 Roger

> (Controllers may issue a revised
> clearance at this point.)

6.7.4   Pilots should report that they are unable to comply with a clearance as a result of a TCAS alert.

> Fastair 345 unable to comply,
> TCAS RA

> Fastair 345 Roger

In these circumstances the pilot should report when clear of the TCAS conflict.

6.8   RADAR ASSISTANCE TO AIRCRAFT WITH RADIO COMMUNICATIONS FAILURE

6.8.1   When a controller suspects that an aircraft is able to receive but not transmit messages, the radar may be used to confirm that the pilot has received instructions. When further instructions are given they should be passed slowly, clearly and be repeated.

> G-CD reply not received if
> you read Wrayton turn left
> heading 040 I say again
> turn left heading 040

> G-CD turn observed I will
> continue to pass instructions

> or

> Fastair 345 reply not
> received if you read Wrayton
> squawk ident I say again
> squawk ident

> Fastair 345 squawk observed
> I will continue to pass
> instructions

*Notes: 1 An aircraft experiencing a radio communications failure is
expected to select the appropriate SSR code.*
2 See also Chapter 9.

6.9 DANGER AREA CROSSING SERVICE/DANGER AREA ACTIVITY INFORMATION SERVICE

6.9.1 In-flight information on the status of Danger Areas (DAs) is available from the nominated service units:

(a) Listed in the UK AIP.

(b) Detailed on the legend of the appropriate UK 1:500 000 Aeronautical Chart.

6.9.2 When available the DA service will either be a Danger Area Crossing Service (DACS) or a Danger Area Activity Information Service (DAAIS). If there is no reply from the appropriate nominated service unit which is to be called for these services, pilots are advised to assume that the relevant danger area is active.

6.9.3 **Danger Area Crossing Service**

The appropriate nominated service unit will, whenever the DA activity permits, provide a clearance for an aircraft to cross the danger area under a RIS or FIS. The clearance is only in relation to Danger Area activity and does not, in traffic management terms, constitute separation from aircraft which might be operating in the area.

Westbury Approach, G-ABCD request Danger Area Crossing Service of Loudwater Range

G-ABCD Westbury Approach Flight Information Service. Loudwater active. Report 10 miles from Loudwater

Wilco G-ABCD

Westbury Approach G-ABCD 10 miles from Loudwater

G-CD Loudwater remains active. Suggest you re-route

Re-routing to the east of Loudwater and changing to Wrayton Information 125.75 G-ABCD

G-ABCD

or

G-ABCD Westbury Approach. Loudwater not active, range crossing approved report vacating the range

Range crossing approved. Wilco G-ABCD

G-ABCD vacating Loudwater Range

77

G-CD Westbury Approach roger, Flight Information available from Wrayton on 125.75

Changing to Wrayton on 125.75 G-CD

6.9.4 Danger Area Activity Information Service

The nominated service unit will pass to the pilot, on request, an update on the known activity status of the danger area. Such an update will assist the pilot to decide whether it would be prudent, on flight safety grounds, to penetrate the Danger Area. A DAAIS does NOT constitute a clearance to cross a Danger Area.

Westbury Approach
G-ABCD request DAAIS for
Loudwater Range

G-ABCD Westbury Approach
Loudwater Active/Not Active

Loudwater Active/Not Active
G-ABCD

6.9.5   Full details of DACS/DAAIS can be found in the UK AIP and AICs.

Chapter 7 – Approach Control

7.1   IFR DEPARTURES

7.1.1   At many airports both arrivals and departures are handled by a single approach control unit. At busier airports departures and arrivals may be handled separately.

7.1.2   Pilots of all aircraft flying Instrument Departures are to include the following information on first contact with approach control/departure radar:

(1)   Call sign;
(2)   SID Designator where appropriate;
(3)   Current or passing ALT/FL; PLUS
(4)   Cleared ALT/FL. For Standard Instrument Departures involving stepped climb profiles, state the initial ALT/FL to which the aircraft is climbing.

7.1.3   In addition to the ATC route clearance, departing IFR flights may be given additional instructions to provide separation in the immediate vicinity.

Fastair 345 Stourton Approach continue heading 040 until passing FL 70 then route direct Wicken	Heading 040 until passing FL 70 then direct Wicken Fastair 345
	Fastair 345 report passing FL 70
	Fastair 345 passing FL 70 routeing direct Wicken
	Fastair 345 contact Wrayton Control 129.1
	Wrayton Control 129.1 Fastair 345

79

7.2 VFR DEPARTURES

7.2.1 Departing VFR flights, when handled by approach control, may be passed information on relevant known traffic in order to assist the pilot in maintaining his own separation. Pilots should report leaving the area of jurisdiction of the approach control units.

> Borton Approach G-CD
> passing the zone boundary

> G-CD Flight Information
> available from Wrayton
> 125.75

> Wrayton Information 125.75
> G-CD

7.2.2 Special VFR flights will be given specific instructions in the clearance to leave the control zone.

> G-CD cleared to the zone
> boundary route via Whiskey
> Special VFR not above
> altitude 1500 feet

> Cleared to the zone
> boundary, route via Whiskey
> Special VFR not above
> altitude 1500 feet G-CD

> G-CD correct

7.3 IFR ARRIVALS

7.3.1 Aircraft flying within controlled airspace will normally receive descent clearance to the clearance limit from the ACC prior to transfer to an approach control unit. On transfer to approach control further descent instructions may be given.

> Kennington Approach
> Fastair 345 descending FL 90
> Information Charlie

> Fastair 345 Kennington
> Approach cleared direct to
> North Cross descend FL 50

> Direct to North Cross
> descend FL 50 Fastair 345

7.3.2 Arriving IFR flights operating outside controlled airspace are not permitted to enter controlled airspace until cleared to do so. Clearances will be given in a way similar to that in paragraph 7.3.1

above. In the examples below the initial approach fix is Kennington NDB (or VOR), callsign KTN.

Kennington Approach
Fastair 345

Fastair 345 Kennington
Approach pass your message

Fastair 345 from Stourton
25 miles southeast
Kennington IFR, FL 125
estimating zone boundary 20
KTN 24 information Charlie

Fastair 345 cleared from
10 miles southeast of
Kennington to KTN at FL 60.
Enter controlled airspace at
FL 85 or below

Cleared from 10 miles
southeast of Kennington to
KTN at FL 60. Enter
controlled airspace southeast
of Kennington at FL 85 or
below Fastair 345

Fastair 345 expect ILS
approach runway 28 QNH
1011

ILS runway 28 QNH 1011
Request straight in approach
Fastair 345

Fastair 345 cleared straight in
ILS approach runway 28,
descend to altitude 3000 feet
QNH 1011, report
established on the localiser

Cleared straight in ILS
approach runway 28 descend
to altitude 3000 feet QNH
1011, Wilco Fastair 345

Fastair 345 established on
the localiser

Fastair 345 QFE 1008

QFE 1008 Fastair 345 runway
in sight

Fastair 345 number 1 contact
Tower 118.7

Number 1 Tower 118.7
Fastair 345

Kennington Tower Fastair 345

Fastair 345 Kennington
Tower report outer marker

Fastair 345

Fastair 345 outer marker

Fastair 345 cleared to land
runway 28 surface wind 280 8

Cleared to land runway 28
Fastair 345

Kennington Approach
G-DCAB

G-DCAB Kennington
Approach pass your message

G-DCAB PA 31 inbound from
Stourton IFR FL 80 estimate
KTN 47 information Delta

G-AB remain outside
controlled airspace. Time is
41. Expect joining clearance
at 44

Remain outside controlled
airspace, G-AB

G-AB cleared from 10 miles
southeast of Kennington to
KTN at FL 80

Cleared from 10 miles
southeast of Kennington to
KTN at FL 80 G-AB

G-AB expect ILS approach
runway 28

G-AB

G-AB descend to altitude
3000 feet QNH 1011

Descend to altitude
3000 feet QNH 1011 G-AB

G-AB cleared ILS approach
runway 28 report KTN
outbound

Cleared ILS runway 28, Wilco
G-AB

G-AB KTN outbound

G-AB report procedure turn
complete QFE 1008

Wilco, QFE 1008 G-AB

G-AB procedure turn
complete localiser established

G-AB report at outer marker

Wilco G-AB

G-AB outer marker

G-AB contact Tower 118.9

Tower 118.9 G-AB

*Note: Pilots may be requested to change to tower frequency at any
point on final approach.*

7.3.3   On occasions IFR aircraft do not complete the instrument approach
procedure but request permission to make a visual approach.

G-AB over KTN 3000 feet
field in sight, request visual
approach

G-AB cleared visual approach
runway 28 QFE 1008 contact
Tower 118.7

QFE 1008 Tower 118.7 G-AB

7.3.4　Normally a holding procedure is published. However, the pilot may require a detailed description of a specific holding procedure.

> Fastair 345 hold at
> North Cross FL 60 expect
> onward clearance at time 40

> Hold at North Cross FL 60,
> request holding procedure
> Fastair 345

> Fastair 345 hold at
> North Cross FL 60 inbound
> track 265 degrees turns left
> outbound time 1 minute

It should be noted that the above information is passed in the following order and is for holds *other* than VOR/DME:

(a)　Fix

(b)　Level

(c)　Inbound track

(d)　Right or left turns

(e)　Time of leg

Holding information for VOR/DME substitutes DISTANCE for TIME in (e) above:

> Fastair 345 request holding
> procedure

> Fastair 345 hold on the
> Marlow *VOR/DME* at 20 DME
> FL 100 inbound track
> 265 degrees turns left,
> limiting outbound distance
> 24 DME

7.4　VFR ARRIVALS

7.4.1　Depending on the procedures in use, the pilot of an arriving VFR flight may be required to establish contact with the approach control unit and request instructions before entering its area of jurisdiction eg before entering a control zone. Where there is an ATIS broadcast the pilot should acknowledge that he has received it; where no ATIS broadcast is provided the approach controller will pass the aerodrome data.

| Kennington Approach G-DCDN | G-DCDN Kennington Approach pass your message |

G-DCDN C172 inbound from Stourton VFR 2500 feet regional QNH 1011 estimating zone boundary 52 Kennington 02 information golf

G-DN cleared from the zone boundary to Kennington VFR, at 2500 feet Kennington QNH 1012. Traffic information there is a southbound Cherokee 2000 feet VFR estimating zone boundary 53

Cleared from the zone boundary to Kennington VFR at 2500 feet QNH 1012, traffic in sight G-DN

G-DN report aerodrome in sight

Wilco G-DN

G-DN aerodrome in sight

G-DN contact Tower 118.5

Tower 118.5 G-DN

Note: The phraseology for joining the aerodrome traffic circuit is detailed in Chapter 4.

7.5   SPECIAL VFR FLIGHTS

7.5.1   Special VFR clearances are only issued for flights within Control Zones and are normally at the request of the pilot. The pilot –

(a)   must comply with ATC instructions;

(b)   is responsible for ensuring that his flight conditions enable him to remain clear of cloud, determine his flight path with reference to the surface and to keep clear of obstructions;

(c)   is responsible for ensuring that he flies within the limitations of his licence;

(d)   is responsible for complying with the relevant low flying restrictions of Rule 5 of the Rules of the Air Regulations. Note: Whilst the 1500 ft rule may not apply to a pilot in receipt of a Special VFR clearance, the 'alight clear' rule always applies. The responsibility to determine whether to accept a Special VFR clearance and still comply with this rule rests with the pilot.

(e)   is responsible for avoiding aerodrome traffic zones unless prior permission for penetration has been obtained from the relevant ATSU.

7.5.2   A full flight plan is not required for Special VFR flight but the pilot must give brief details of the callsign, aircraft type and pilot's intentions, including ETA at entry point. A full flight plan is required if the pilot wishes his destination to be notified.

7.5.3   Aircraft are not normally given a specific height to fly but vertical separation from aircraft flying above can be achieved by requiring the Special VFR flight to fly not above a specified level (Section (d) above must be borne in mind by pilots).

7.5.4   No separation will be provided between Special VFR flights which are flying in notified areas or routes where an individual clearance is not required, or between flights using such areas or routes and other flights on Special VFR clearances. Full details of the procedures for Special VFR flights appear in the UK AIP, ENR, Section 1.

7.6   RADAR VECTORS TO FINAL APPROACH

7.6.1   Radar vectors are given to arriving flights to position them onto a pilot-interpreted approach aid, to a point from which a radar-assisted approach can be made or to a point from which a visual approach is made. In the following example an identified aircraft inbound to Kennington is given radar vectors to the ILS. (See fig 2.)

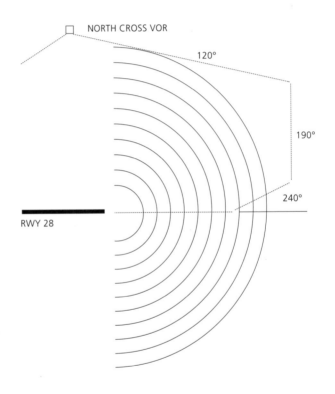

Figure 2 Radar vectors to an ILS approach

Kennington Approach
Fastair 345 FL 60 information
Golf

Fastair 345 Kennington
Approach vectoring for
ILS approach runway 28

Fastair 345

Fastair 345 leave North Cross
heading 120

Leave North Cross heading
120 Fastair 345

Fastair 345 report speed

Fastair 345 speed 260 knots

Fastair 345 reduce speed to
210 knots

210 knots Fastair 345

Fastair 345 leaving North
Cross heading 120

Fastair 345 Roger descend to
altitude 2500 feet QNH 1011
number 4 in traffic

Descend to altitude
2500 feet QNH 1011
Fastair 345

Fastair 345 position 10 miles
northeast of Kennington.
This is a right hand circuit
for runway 28

Fastair 345

Fastair 345 turn right heading 190 base leg, no ATC speed restrictions

Right heading 190. No speed restriction Fastair 345

Fastair 345 12 miles from touchdown turn right heading 240 closing localiser from the right report established

Right heading 240 ILS Wilco Fastair 345

Fastair 345 localiser established

Fastair 345 descend on the ILS QFE 1008

Wilco, QFE 1008 Fastair 345

Fastair 345 contact Tower 118.5

Tower 118.5 Fastair 345

7.6.2　In the example above the approach speed of the aircraft is reduced to maintain separation between aircraft in an approach sequence. Where speed adjustment would be insufficient, it may be necessary to issue additional vectors.

Fastair 345 delaying action make a 360 turn to the left	360 turn to the left Fastair 345
Fastair turn left heading 220 for spacing	Left heading 220 Fastair 345

7.7   DIRECTION FINDING (DF)

7.7.1   The aeronautical stations that offer a VHF Direction Finding (VDF) service are listed in the UK AIP AD. Some VDF stations stipulate that the service is not available for en-route navigation purposes (except in emergency). VDF bearing information will only be given when conditions are satisfactory and radio bearings fall within calibrated limits of the station. If the provision of a radio bearing is not possible the pilot will be told of the reason.

A pilot may request a bearing or heading using the appropriate phrase or Q code to specify the service required. Each aircraft transmission shall be ended by the aircraft call sign. A VDF station will provide the following as requested:

(1)   QDR – Magnetic bearing of the aircraft from the station (ie .....
Approach G-ABCD request QDR G-ABCD).

(2)   QDM – Magnetic heading to be steered by the aircraft (assuming no wind) to reach the VDF station (ie ..... Approach G-ABCD request QDM G-ABCD).

(3)   QTE – True bearing of the aircraft from the station (ie .....
Approach G-ABCD request True Bearing (or QTE) G-ABCD).

The direction-finding station will reply in the following manner:

(1)   The appropriate phrase or Q code.

(2)   The bearing or heading in degrees in relation to the direction-finding station.

(3)   The class of bearing.

(4)   The time of observation, if necessary.

Kennington Approach G-DCAB request QDM G-DCAB	G-DCAB Kennington Approach QDM 090 degrees class Bravo
	QDM 090 degrees class Bravo G-DCAB
True bearing, true bearing, Kennington Approach G-DCAB request true bearing G-DCAB	G-DCAB Kennington Approach true bearing 276 degrees true, I say again, 276 degrees true, class bravo
	True bearing 276 degrees class Bravo G-DCAB

7.7.2   The accuracy of the observation is classified as follows:

Class A – Accurate within plus or minus 2 degrees

Class B – Accurate within plus or minus 5 degrees

Class C – Accurate within plus or minus 10 degrees

Class D – Accuracy less than Class C

Note: Normally no better than Class B bearing will be available.

7.8   QGH PROCEDURE

7.8.1   QGH letdowns may be provided, when requested by a pilot, at aerodromes where the procedure is approved. The procedure provides for control of an aircraft from its initial approach level to a position from which an approach can be completed visually (see figure 3); this approach may not be aligned with a runway.

7.8.2   On receiving a request for a QGH the aircraft is to be homed overhead the VDF aerial at or descending to the lowest available flight level/

altitude taking into account the minimum safe flight level or safety altitude as appropriate. During homing the following message will be passed to the pilot:

G-ABCD, Kennington Approach set heading 230, maintain FL 40 (procedure minimum 670 feet (if requested))	Turning left heading 230 maintaining FL 40 (procedure minimum 670 feet), FL 40, G-ABCD

7.8.3   During the procedure aircraft replies are used to obtain D/F bearings. Pilots may be asked to make additional transmissions for D/F. With some equipment the full callsign is sufficient to obtain bearings.

G-ABCD transmit for D/F	G-ABCD transmitting for D/F G-ABCD

or

G-ABCD

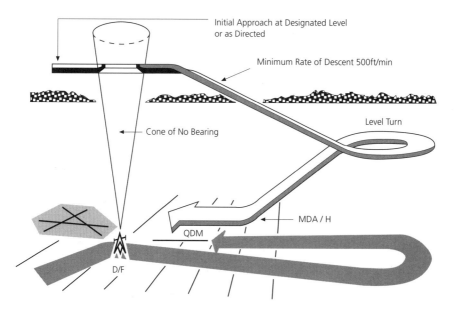

Figure 3 QGH procedure

7.8.4   Two D/F indications are required to confirm the aircraft is overhead the VDF aerial; then instructions are given to achieve the desired outbound track.

G-ABCD transmit for overhead	G-ABCD transmitting for D/F G-ABCD
	G-ABCD transmit for overhead
	G-ABCD transmitting for D/F G-ABCD
	G-ABCD indicating overhead turn left heading 105 report steady
	Left heading 105. Wilco. G-ABCD
	G-ABCD steady heading 105

7.8.5   On completion of the overhead turn and when bearings indicate the aircraft is outbound the controller starts timing the outbound leg and provides heading corrections derived from a series of bearings to make good the desired outbound track. Descent instructions and the appropriate pressure setting are also given during this procedure.

G-ABCD set QNH 1011	QNH 1011 G-ABCD
	G-ABCD descend to altitude 2500 feet. Report level
	Descend to altitude 2500 feet wilco G-ABCD

7.8.6   On completion of the timed outbound leg (eg 3 min) the aircraft is instructed to turn onto a heading to achieve the final approach track.

G-ABCD turn left heading 270, report steady	Left heading 270 Wilco G-ABCD

7.8.7   When the aircraft reports steady on completion of the inbound turn, headings will continue to be given to achieve the inbound track. During the inbound leg the controller will pass instructions to be followed in the event of a missed approach (Note: At military airfields the weather and missed approach procedure may be passed at an earlier stage in the procedure). Descent clearance to minimum descent height and the QFE will be given on this leg.

G-ABCD in the event of a missed approach climb straight ahead to altitude 2500 feet, turn right and hold at the KTN	In the event of a missed approach climb straight ahead to altitude 2500 feet, turn right and hold at the KTN, G-ABCD
	G-ABCD set QFE 1008
	QFE 1008 G-ABCD
G-ABCD continue descent to minimum descent height. Report field in sight	Descend to minimum descent height, Wilco G-ABCD

7.8.8   If the pilot has not reported 'visual' by the time minimum descent height is reached he may be instructed to maintain level flight until he is overhead the VDF.

If the aircraft is not 'visual' when overhead the VDF, the controller will give the instruction to carry out a missed approach procedure.

7.9   VDF PROCEDURE

7.9.1   This is a procedure whereby a pilot requests a series of QDMs to home to a VDF station or or near an aerodrome and to carry out a prescribed VDF instrument approach procedure to the aerodrome. VDF procedures are notified in the AD section of the UK AIP.

7.9.2   Requests for QDMs are normally initiated by the pilot at intervals of about 1 minute during the initial stages of the homing, increasing in frequency as the VDF overhead is approach. During this procedure QDMs are requested as required to achieve and maintain the specified tracks. *The VDF Procedure is totally pilot interpreted.*

> Borton Approach, G-ABCD, information Delta, request homing and VDF approach

> G-ABCD, Borton Approach, pass your message

> G-ABCD, T67, 15 miles northwest of Borton, heading 130, FL 55, IFR, inbound Borton, request homing and VDF approach, G-ABCD

> G-ABCD, cleared to the VDF overhead at altitude 3000 feet Borton QNH 1010, QDM 120 class Bravo, report overhead

> Cleared to the VDF overhead at altitude 3000 feet Borton QNH 1010, QDM 120 class Bravo, Wilco, G-ABCD

7.9.3   The pilot employs a series of QDMs to home to the VDF overhead positioning himself to arrive from a direction which will entail the minimum of manoeuvring in the overhead to proceed outbound on the specified track.

G-ABCD request QDM
G-ABCD

G-ABCD QDM 120

QDM 120 G-ABCD

G-ABCD maintaining
3000 feet, request QDM
G-ABCD

G-ABCD Roger, QDM 130

QDM 130 G-ABCD

G-ABCD request QDM,
G-ABCD

G-ABCD QDM 145, cleared
VDF approach runway 34

QDM 145, cleared VDF
approach runway 34 G-ABCD

G-ABCD request QDM
G-ABCD

G-ABCD QDM 150

QDM 150 G-ABCD

G-ABCD request QDM
G-ABCD

G-ABCD no bearing

G-ABCD request QDM
G-ABCD

G-ABCD no bearing

G-ABCD overhead turning
outbound G-ABCD

G-ABCD report descending
in the procedure QFE 1007

Wilco, QFE 1007 G-ABCD

7.9.4   The pilot starts timing the outbound leg and, employing a series of
         QDMs to establish and maintain the prescribed track, descends as
         notified for the procedure. The timed outbound leg ends with a turn
         (normally level) onto the final approach QDM.

G-ABCD request QDM
G-ABCD

G-ABCD QDM 340

G-ABCD descending
outbound QDM 340 G-ABCD

G-ABCD Roger, report base
turn complete

Wilco G-ABCD

G-ABCD request QDM
G-ABCD

G-ABCD QDM 350

QDM 350 G-ABCD

7.9.5   At the end of the outbound leg the pilot turns as prescribed onto the final approach QDM using a series of QDMs during the turn to achieve the final QDM.

G-ABCD request QDM
G-ABCD

G-ABCD QDM 345

QDM 345 G-ABCD

G-ABCD request QDM
G-ABCD

G-ABCD QDM 342

QDM 342 G-ABCD

G-ABCD base turn complete,
descending inbound,
G-ABCD

G-ABCD continue approach,
report field in sight
QFE 1007

G-ABCD Wilco, QFE 1007,
request QDM G-ABCD

G-ABCD QDM 338

QDM 338 G-ABCD

G-ABCD request QDM
G-ABCD

G-ABCD QDM 340

QDM 340 G-ABCD

G-ABCD field in sight

G-ABCD contact Tower 118.7

Tower 118.7 G-ABCD

7.9.6   If no visual contact is gained, a missed approach is initiated at the
missed approach point which is normally the VDF overhead.

G-ABCD request QDM
G-ABCD

G-ABCD no bearing

G-ABCD nothing seen,
initiating missed approach
procedure G-ABCD

7.10   NDB(L) AND VOR PROCEDURES

7.10.1   NDB(L) and VOR instrument approach procedures are pilot
interpreted procedures notified for particular aerodromes and runways
where procedural tracks are defined by NDB(L) bearings or VOR
radials. Some NDB(L) and VOR procedures may include marker
beacons or DME to provide ranging information. Aircraft may also be
radar vectored to an NDB(L) or VOR final approach track. An example
of a typical NDB(L) instrument approach procedure to an aerodrome
outside controlled airspace follows; similar RT phraseology may be
employed in VOR procedures.

Borton Approach, G-ABCD
inbound Borton, information
Delta

G-ABCD, Borton Approach
pass your message

G-ABCD, T67, 20 miles South
of Borton, FL 80, IFR,
estimating BTN 47, request
beacon approach

G-ABCD cleared to BTN at
FL 80, expect beacon
approach RW 34, expected
approach time 58

Cleared to BTN FL 80 to
hold. Expected approach
time 58. G-ABCD

G-CD descend to altitude
3000 feet, Borton QNH 1015,
report entering the hold

Descend to altitude 3000 feet
Borton QNH 1015, wilco,
G-CD

G-CD overhead the BTN,
maintaining 3000 ft entering
the hold

G-CD

Notes: 1 *All manoeuvres associated with entering the holding pattern are considered to be part of the holding procedure.*

2 *Aircraft engaged in holding for training purposes should notify the controller on the commencement of the penultimate hold, eg 'G-CD on completion of this hold, request commence procedure'.*

G-CD cleared beacon
approach runway 34, report
beacon outbound

Cleared for beacon approach
runway 34, Wilco, G-CD

G-CD beacon outbound

Note: Beacon outbound should be called only at the final passage over the beacon when commencing the outbound portion of the procedure.

G-CD report base turn complete, QFE 1013

Wilco, QFE 1013 G-CD

G-CD base turn complete

G-CD report at 4 DME

Wilco, G-CD

G-CD 4 DME

G-CD Roger, contact Tower 118.7

Tower 118.7, G-CD

7.11   SURVEILLANCE RADAR APPROACH (SRA)

7.11.1   During a surveillance radar approach (SRA) the pilot is given distances from touchdown, advisory height information and azimuth instructions to enable him to make an approach to a particular runway. Controllers at civil aerodromes in the UK will normally pass advisory heights based on the QFE.

Fastair 345 this will be a surveillance radar approach terminating at half a mile from touchdown. Check your minima, step down fixes and missed approach point

Fastair 345

Note: Where step down fixes do not exist in local SRAs, dispensation for a modified RT procedure may be sought from ATSSD.

7.11.2　If a pilot wishes to conduct his approach by reference to altitude he must inform the controller and request the QNH. The controller, when passing the QNH, will add the aerodrome or touchdown elevation to the advisory heights. All references to the level of the aircraft will then be to altitude.

7.11.3　If the pilot reports visual in the early stages of the approach he will be asked whether he wishes to continue the SRA. Normally aircraft will not be transferred to aerodrome control until after they have completed the SRA approach and have landed.

7.11.4　The range at which the descent begins depends on the height of the aircraft during the intermediate phase and the angle of the glide path. The following example commences when the aircraft, having been descended to 2000 feet QFE, is awaiting instructions for an approach on a three degree glide path.

Fastair 345 turn right heading 275 final approach	Right heading 275 Fastair 345
Fastair 345, 8 miles from touchdown. Your descent will begin at $6^1/_2$ miles. Check wheels	Fastair 345
Fastair 345.7 miles from touchdown. Report runway or approach lights in sight	Fastair 345
Fastair 345 after landing contact Kennington tower on 118.5	After landing Kennington tower 118.5 Fastair 345
Fastair 345 approaching $6^1/_2$ miles from touchdown. Commence descent now to maintain a three degree glide path	Descending Fastair 345

6 miles from touchdown. Height should be 1850 feet	Fastair 345
Slightly left of track. Turn right heading 280	Heading 280 Fastair 345
5$^1/_2$ miles from touchdown. Height should be 1700 feet	Fastair 345
5 miles from touchdown. Height should be 1550 feet. Heading 280 is good	Fastair 345
4$^1/_2$ miles from touchdown. Height should be 1400 feet. Slightly right of track. Turn left 3 degrees heading 277	Heading 277, Fastair 345
4 miles from touchdown. Height should be 1250 feet. Do not reply to further instructions	

(the gap between further transmissions will be less than 5 seconds)

3$^1/_2$ miles from touchdown. Height should be 1100 feet. Cleared to land runway 28. Surface wind calm

3 miles from touchdown. Height should be 950 feet. Heading 277 is good

$2^1/_2$ miles from touchdown.
Height should be 800 feet.
On track

2 miles from touchdown.
Height should be 650 feet.
Check minimum descent
height

$1^1/_2$ miles from touchdown.
Height should be 500 feet.
On track

1 mile from touchdown.
Height should be 350 feet

On track. Half a mile from
touchdown. Approach
completed. Out

7.11.5   When the SRA terminates at 2 miles from touchdown the advisory level checks at half mile intervals are omitted and pilots are expected to reply to all transmissions from the ground station.

7.11.6   Height checks below the category A aircraft OCH will be omitted.

7.12   LANDING ALTIMETER SETTING (QNE)

QNE is the indication which the altimeter will give on landing, at a particular time and place, when the millibar scale is set to 1013.2 mb. QNE information may be used by pilots of aircraft whose altimeters cannot be set to below 950 mb. The QFE/QNE conversion will be calculated by ATC.

Example: QFE 947.6   Set 1013.2 on altimeter
                        Altimeter will read 1842 ft on touchdown

7.13   PRECISION APPROACH RADAR

7.13.1   Pilots visiting military airfields may wish to undertake a Precision Approach Radar (PAR). The following scenario assumes that G-RRRF has already been identified by Westbury Approach and is under an ATC service at 2500 ft on the Regional QNH.

> Westbury Approach, G-RRRF request PAR

> > G-RF Westbury Approach, PAR for runway 27 approved, procedure minimum 300 ft

> G-RF 300 ft to land

> > G-RF roger, set QFE 1001 descend to 1500 ft

> 1001 set, descend to height 1500 ft, G-RF

> > G-RF are you familiar with Westbury Missed Approach and Communication Failure Procedure

> G-RF negative

> > G-RF in the event of a missed approach, climb straight ahead to the safety height of 2300 ft and recall me on this frequency

> In the event of a missed approach, climb straight ahead to the safety height of 2300 ft and recall Westbury on this frequency, GRF

G-RF correct. If radio contact is lost, or if no transmissions are received for 20 seconds, and you are unable to continue this approach, climb to the safety height of 2300 ft and recall Westbury on this or any other published frequency

If radio contact is lost, or if no transmissions are received for 20 seconds, and am I unable to continue this approach, climb to the safety height of 2300 ft and recall Westbury on this or any other published frequency, G-RF

G-RF correct. Turn right heading 100 downwind

Right heading 100 G-RF

G-RF heading 100, maintaining 1500 ft

G-RF, 5 miles downwind, cockpit checks report complete

G-RF cockpit checks complete

G-RF turn left heading 360 base leg

Left heading 360, G-RF

G-RF heading 360

G-RF turn left heading 310

Left heading 310, G-RF

G-RF heading 310

G-RF turn left heading 265 final approach

Left heading 265, G-RF

G-RF, 8 miles, contact Westbury talkdown on 123.3

Westbury talkdown 123.3 G-RF

Westbury talkdown G-RRRF

G-RF Westbury talkdown identified, turn right heading 270, readback QFE

Right heading 270, QFE 1001 set G-RF

G-RF 7 miles, correcting nicely to the centreline

G-RF

G-RF 6½ miles, slightly right of centreline, turn left heading 265

Left heading 265, G-RF

G-RF when safely on the runway contact Westbury Tower on 132.85

When safely on the runway contact Westbury Tower on 132.85, G-RF

G-RF 6 miles, correcting nicely to the centreline, approaching descent point do not acknowledge further instructions unless requested

5½ miles, heading is good

Turn right 3° heading 268

5 miles begin descent now for a 3° glidepath, on the centreline

Turn right 2° heading 270, on the centreline, slightly above the glidepath

4½ miles heading is good, correcting to the glidepath

On glidepath, on centreline, heading 270

4 miles, slightly below glidepath, check gear acknowledge

Gear down, G-RF

Slightly left of centreline turn right heading 273, correcting nicely to the glidepath

3½ miles, on glidepath, slightly left of centreline

Turn left 3° heading 270 on centreline

3 miles, cleared to land, surface wind 250 5, on glidepath, on centreline heading 270

Turn left 2° heading 268, on centreline, on glidepath

2½ miles, on centreline, on glidepath

2 miles, slightly right of centreline, turn left 3° heading 265, on glidepath

Slightly above glidepath, correcting nicely to the centreline, heading 265

1½ miles, heading is good, correcting to the glidepath

Approaching decision height, on glidepath, on centreline, turn right 3° heading 268

1 mile, on glidepath, on centreline

Slightly above glidepath, on centreline

½ mile, on glidepath on centreline

G-RF over touchdown

G-RF changing to Westbury Tower 132.85

G-RF

7.13.2 The following phrases may also be encountered during a PAR; further explanation of some of the terms employed are included in the Remarks column in the table below:

Position	Control to Aircraft	Aircraft to Control	Remarks
Initial approach	G-RF Westbury, PAR Azimuth only for runway 27 approved, procedure minimum .... ft	.... ft, G-RF	Employed when no glidepath information is available
Glidepath and rate of descent	Well above/below glidepath. Acknowledge G-RF correcting rapidly to glidepath	G-RF	
Range	.... miles		Passed at $\frac{1}{2}$ nm intervals. (RN pass ranges at $\frac{1}{3}$ nm intervals
Heading	Well/slightly left/right of centreline correcting rapidly/slowly/ nicely to centreline		
Glidepath failure during PAR	Glidepath failure, the procedure minimum is .... ft – acknowledge G-RF	G-RF	Procedure continues to published Missed Approach Point for AZ only approach

Position	Control to Aircraft	Aircraft to Control	Remarks
Undercarriage check	Check gear, acknowledge	Gear down, G-RF	Normally carried out between 3 and 4 nm from touchdown. Not required for aircraft with fixed undercarriage
Clearance	Final clearance delayed, continue approach		Indicating that required clearance may be forthcoming
	Break off this approach – acknowledge .... (further instructions as required)	G-RF acknowledged (repeat of any further instructions)	Specific instructions and reasons will be passed

7.14   MILITARY AERODROME TRAFFIC ZONES (MATZ) AND ASSOCIATED PENETRATION SERVICES

7.14.1   Comprehensive details of MATZ and the associated penetration service, including controlling aerodromes, contact frequencies and hours of watch, are contained in the UK AIP ENR Section, AICs, AIP Supplements or System NOTAM.

7.14.2   While every effort will be made to ensure safe separation, some civil aircraft flying within the MATZ may not be known to controllers and therefore pilots should keep a careful look-out at all times.

7.14.3   Pilots requiring a MATZ penetration service must establish two way RT communication on the appropriate frequency with the aerodrome controlling the zone when 15 nm or 5 min flying time from the boundary whichever is the sooner. When asked by the controller to 'pass your message' the pilot should pass the following information:

(a)   Callsign
(b)   Type of aircraft
(c)   Position
(d)   Heading
(e)   Altitude/FL
(f)   Intentions (eg destination)

Westbury Approach G-ABCD request MATZ penetration

G-ABCD Westbury Approach pass your message

G-ABCD, Slingsby from Borton over Middleton heading 350, altitude 2500 feet regional QNH 1005 en-route Walden

G-CD, cross MATZ at 1500 ft on Westbury QFE 1001. Report entering and leaving the MATZ

Cross MATZ at 1500 ft on Westbury QFE 1001, Wilco G-CD

Whilst working a MATZ unit, pilots are expected to comply with any instructions issued by controllers and maintain a listening watch on the allocated RT frequency. They should not change heading or level without giving prior warning and should advise when leaving the MATZ. At some MATZ units, the Zone controller is responsible for MATZ penetration services.

7.15   LOWER AIRSPACE RADAR SERVICE (LARS)

7.15.1   LARS is available to assist pilots flying outside controlled airspace up to and including FL 95. LARS is normally provided within 30 nm of the nominated unit and is provided at the discretion of the controller. Therefore, when primary task loadings are high, LARS may not be available. The services available are **Radar Advisory Service (RAS)** or **Radar Information Service (RIS)**; the type of service required should be specified as detailed at para 7.15.3 below.

7.15.2   Pilots requiring a LARS should establish RT communication with the appropriate ATSU using the following format:

> Westbury Approach
> G-ABCD request Lower
> Airspace Radar Service

> G-ABCD Westbury Approach
> pass your message

7.15.3   Once communications have been established the pilot should pass the following details:

(a)   Callsign and type of aircraft

(b)   Point of departure and estimated position

(c)   Heading

(d)   Level (or level and band for traffic wishing to carry out general handling)

(e)   Intention (next reporting/turning point, destination etc)

(f)   The flight rules under which he is operating and the type of service required (RAS or RIS)

> G-ABCD, T67, 15 miles SE
> Westbury heading 350, FL45,
> IFR, destination Walden,
> request Radar Advisory
> Service

7.15.4   The identification procedure does not imply that a radar service is being provided. The pilot must not assume that he is in receipt of a RAS or RIS until the controller has made a positive statement to that effect based on an 'accord' being reached between the pilot and the controller of the type of service to be provided.

7.15.5   RAS and RIS are defined as follows:

(a)   **RAS.** RAS is an air traffic radar service in which the controller will provide advice necessary to maintain prescribed separation between aircraft participating in the advisory service, and in which he will pass to the pilot the bearing, distance and, if known, level of conflicting non-participating traffic, together with advice on action necessary to resolve the confliction. Where time does not permit this procedure to be adopted, the controller will pass advice on avoiding action followed by information on the conflicting traffic. Under a RAS the following conditions apply:

(i)   The service will only be provided to flights under IFR irrespective of meteorological conditions.

(ii)   Controllers will expect the pilot to accept vectors or level allocations which may require flight in IMC. **Pilots not qualified to fly in IMC should accept a RAS only where compliance with ATC advice permits the flight to be continued in VMC;**

(iii)   There is no legal requirement for a pilot flying outside Controlled Airspace to comply with instructions because of the advisory nature of the service. However, a pilot who chooses not to comply with advisory avoiding action must inform the controller. The pilot will then become responsible for initiating any avoiding action that may subsequently prove necessary.

(iv)   The pilot must advise the controller before changing heading or level.

(v)   The avoiding action instructions which a controller may pass to resolve a confliction with non-participating traffic will, where possible, be aimed at achieving separation which is not less than 5nm or 5000ft, except when specified otherwise by the regulating authority. However, it is recognised that in the event of the sudden appearance of unknown traffic, and when unknown aircraft make

116

unpredictable changes in flight path, it is not always possible to achieve these minima.

(vi) Information on conflicting traffic will be passed until the confliction is resolved.

(vii) The pilot remains responsible for terrain clearance, although ATSUs providing a RAS will set a level or levels below which a RAS will be refused or terminated.

(b) **RIS.** RIS is an air traffic radar service in which the controller will inform the pilot of the bearing, distance and, if known, the level of the conflicting traffic. No avoiding action will be offered. **The pilot is wholly responsible for maintaining separation from other aircraft whether or not the controller has passed traffic information.** Under a RIS the following conditions apply:

(i) The service may be requested under any flight rules or meteorological conditions.

(ii) The controller will only update details of conflicting traffic after the initial warning, at the pilot's request, or if the controller considers that the conflicting traffic continues to constitute a definite hazard.

(iii) The controller may provide radar vectors for the purpose of tactical planning or at the request of the pilot. However, vectors will not be provided to maintain separation from other aircraft, which remains the responsibility of the pilot. There is no requirement for a pilot to accept vectors.

(iv) The pilot must advise the controller before changing level, level band or route.

(v) RIS may be offered when the provision of RAS is impracticable.

(vi) Request for a RIS to be changed to a RAS will be accepted subject to the controller's workload; prescribed separation will be applied as soon as practicable. If a RAS cannot be provided the controller will continue to offer a RIS.

(vii) For manoeuvring flights which involve frequent changes of heading or flight level, RIS may be requested by the pilot or offered by the controller. Information on conflicting traffic will be passed with reference to cardinal points. The pilot must indicate the level band within which he wishes to operate and is responsible for selecting the manoeuvring area, but may request the controller's assistance in finding a suitable location. The controller may suggest re-positioning on his own initiative, but the pilot is not bound to comply.

(viii) The pilot remains responsible for terrain clearance. ATSUs providing a RIS will set a level or levels below which vectors will not be provided, except when specified otherwise by the regulating authority.

7.15.6   Details of LARS, including participating ATSUs, their hours of operation and contact frequencies, are contained in the UK AIP ENR Section and AICs.

Chapter 8 – Area Control

8.1 AREA CONTROL CENTRES

8.1.1 The following examples of phraseology are suitable for use at area control centres according to the requirements of the prevailing traffic situation.

Fastair 345 request descent

Fastair 345 maintain FL 280 expect descent after Marlow

Maintaining FL 280 Fastair 345

Fastair 345 descend FL 120. Cross Colinton FL 170 or above

Descend FL 120. Cross Colinton FL 170 or above Fastair 345

Fastair 345 are you able to cross Colinton at time 52

Affirm Fastair 345

Fastair 345 cross Colinton not before time 52

Cross Colinton not before time 52 Fastair 345

8.2 POSITION INFORMATION

8.2.1 In order to assist in establishing separation, pilots may be instructed to provide additional position report information as well as routine reports.

Fastair 345 report Colinton

Fastair 345

Fastair 345 Colinton 47
FL 170 descending FL 120,
abeam KTN at 55

Fastair 345

Fastair 345 report 25 miles
DME from Kennington

Wilco Fastair 345

Fastair 345 report your DME
distance from Kennington

Fastair 345 26 miles

Fastair 345 report crossing
radial 270 Kennington VOR

Wilco Fastair 345

8.3   FLIGHTS JOINING AIRWAYS

8.3.1   Aircraft requiring to join an airway should make their request to the
appropriate ATSU. Where no flight plan has been filed, the request
should include the filing of an airborne flight plan (see Chapter 3). Where
a flight plan has already been filed an abbreviated call may be made.

Wrayton Control G-RDVC
request clearance to enter
controlled airspace northeast
of Marlow at FL 240 at time
42

G-RDVC cleared at time 42
from 8 miles northeast of
Marlow to Colinton via A1,
maintain FL 240, squawk
5507

Cleared at time 42 from
8 miles northeast of Marlow
to Colinton, via A1, maintain
FL 240, squawk 5507 G-RDVC

G-RDVC correct

8.3.2   Because of the prevailing traffic situation, a joining clearance may not
be issued immediately.

120

> G-RDVC remain outside controlled airspace expect joining clearance at time 55 time is 44

> Remaining outside controlled airspace G-RDVC

8.3.3 In the event that the requested flight level is already occupied the controller will offer an alternative.

> G-RDVC request FL 240

> G-RDVC unable approve FL 240, FL 220 available

> G-RDVC accept FL 220

8.4   FLIGHTS LEAVING AIRWAYS

8.4.1 Flights leaving controlled airspace will normally be given a specific point at which to leave, together with any other relevant instructions necessary to ensure separation.

> G-RDVC cleared to leave controlled airspace northeast of Marlow at FL 220 whilst in controlled airspace

> Cleared to leave controlled airspace northeast Marlow at FL 220 in controlled airspace G-RDVC

8.4.2 An aircraft may request permission to leave controlled airspace by descent.

> G-RDVC request permission to leave controlled airspace by descent

> G-RDVC cleared to leave controlled airspace by descent. Report passing altitude 5500 feet Regional Pressure Setting 1014

> Cleared to leave controlled airspace by descent will report passing altitude 5500 feet Regional Pressure Setting 1014 G-RDVC

In the above example the base of the airway is 5500 feet.

121

8.5 FLIGHTS CROSSING AIRWAYS

8.5.1 An aircraft requiring to cross an airway should make its request to the appropriate ATSU.

> Wrayton Control G-ABCD request crossing of A1 at Wicken

> G-ABCD Wrayton Control pass your message

> G-ABCD T67 from Borton, 20 miles north of Wicken heading 220 FL 80 IMC request crossing clearance of airway A1 at Wicken FL 80 at 1033

> G-ABCD cleared to cross A1 at Wicken, maintain FL 80 whilst in controlled airspace. Report entering the airway

> Cleared to cross A1 at Wicken maintain FL 80 in controlled airspace. Wilco. G-ABCD

8.6 FLIGHTS HOLDING EN-ROUTE

8.6.1 When an aircraft is required to hold en-route, the controller will issue holding instructions and a time at which onward clearance can be expected. Where it is not self-evident, the reason for the delay should also be given.

> Fastair 345 hold at Colinton FL 170, expect onward clearance at 03, landing delays at Kennington 20 minutes

> Hold at Colinton FL 170 expect onward clearance at time 03 Fastair 345

Chapter 9 – Emergency RT Procedures

9.1 INTRODUCTION

9.1.1 This chapter describes the characteristics of the VHF International Aeronautical Emergency Service and the RT procedures which should be used under the Aeronautical Mobile Service during an emergency in the UK. Additional information is published in the UK AIP (GEN) section and AICs.

9.2 STATES OF EMERGENCY

9.2.1 The states of emergency are classified as follows:

(1) *Distress* A condition of being threatened by serious and/or imminent danger and of requiring immediate assistance.

(2) *Urgency* A condition concerning the safety of an aircraft or other vehicle, or of some person on board or within sight, but does not require immediate assistance.

9.2.2 The pilot should make the appropriate emergency call as follows:

(1) *Distress* 'MAYDAY, MAYDAY, MAYDAY This is ---- (Aircraft Callsign)'

(2) *Urgency* 'PAN PAN, PAN PAN, PAN PAN This is ---- (Aircraft Callsign)'

9.3 VHF EMERGENCY SERVICE

9.3.1 Characteristics of the service

9.3.1.1 The UK has two Distress and Diversion (D&D) Sections located at the London and Scottish Area Control Centres. They are manned by RAF control staff who are assisted in the provision of an emergency service on the International Aeronautical Emergency Frequency 121.50 MHz by suitably equipped civil and military units and certain HM Coastguard stations. The service is available continuously to pilots flying within UK airspace who are in distress, in urgent need of assistance, or experiencing difficulties, (ie temporarily unsure of position) which could lead to a state of emergency. The service may also be available for practices provided that no actual emergency is in progress on the UHF or VHF distress frequencies. More information on the emergency service for civil pilots can be found in the UK AIP (GEN).

9.3.1.2   The primary role of the D&D Sections is to provide military and civil pilots with an emergency aid and position fixer service. Autotriangulation (DF) coverage on 121.5 MHz is available over most of the London FIR above 2000 ft amsl to aircraft flying to the east and south of Manchester. In respect of other civil aircraft incidents on VHF they rely for position fixing on DF bearing information obtained by telephone from external units equipped with VDF. This fixing procedure takes time and may require several minutes of concentrated activity because it involves the manual plotting onto 1:250,000 charts of the bearings received. The quality of the position fixes is determined by the availability of VDF bearings, and thus, depends largely on the height of an aircraft and its distance from the VDF stations. The coverage of the VHF fixing service is limited below 3000 ft amsl; indeed, the ability to locate aircraft at low altitude by the use of VDF may be severely inhibited (because of the effects of high ground) over much of Scotland, Wales and SW England. In circumstances where 121.5 MHz DF data is lacking, the controller's ability to assist a pilot who is uncertain of his position is very limited, and will depend on such factors as the availability of SSR information and the amount and accuracy of the information provided by the pilot about his route, last known position and observed landmarks.

9.3.1.3   Certain UK aerodromes can also offer civil pilots an effective emergency communications and aid service. Some maintain a continuous watch on 121.50 MHz, but not all are equipped with VDF or SSR. Others do not normally listen out on 121.50 MHz but they do have VDF and may be asked by the Emergency Controller to provide DF bearing information on an aircraft, and other assistance. Where a bearing is required for fixing purposes from an airfield which has VDF but not on 121.5 MHz, the Emergency Controller may instruct the pilot to change temporarily to the frequency on which VDF is available.

9.4 USE OF THE SERVICE – GENERAL PROCEDURES

9.4.1 Pilots should address their emergency calls on 121.50 MHz to 'London Centre' when south of N55°, and 'Scottish Centre' when north of N55°. If doubt exists about the appropriate centre, it is not necessary to address a specific station. Once two-way communication has been established, pilots should not leave 121.5 MHz without telling the controller. The use of special D&D Sections at the ACCs in the provision of emergency services is unique to the UK. Detailed information on related UK Search and Rescue (SAR) procedures is contained in the GEN Section of the UK AIP.

9.4.2 Pilots are urged – in their own interests – to request assistance from the emergency service as soon as there is any doubt about the safe conduct of their flight. Even then, the provision of assistance may be delayed if a pilot does not pass clear details of his difficulties and requirements, using the international standard RT prefix 'MAYDAY, MAYDAY, MAYDAY' or 'PAN PAN, PAN PAN, PAN PAN' as appropriate. For example, a vague request from a pilot for 'confirmation of position' is unlikely to be accorded as much priority as would be given to a statement that he is lost. If, subsequent to the transmission of a 'MAYDAY' or 'PAN', a pilot considers the problem not to be as serious as first thought and priority attention is no longer required, the emergency condition may be cancelled at the pilot's discretion. It is invariably preferable for pilots believing themselves to be facing emergency situations to declare them as early as possible and then cancel later if they decide the situation allows.

9.4.3 If a pilot is already in communication with a civil or military ATSU, before the emergency arises, assistance should be requested from the controller on the frequency in use. In this case, any SSR code setting previously assigned by ATC (other than the Conspicuity Code 7000) should be retained until instructions are received to change the code setting.

9.4.4 If, however, the pilot is not in direct communication with an ATSU and the aircraft is equipped with an SSR transponder it should be switched, preferably before the emergency call is made, to Mode A Emergency Code 7700, with Mode C if available. If the transponding aircraft is high enough to be within secondary radar cover, the selection of the Emergency 7700 Code will alert the Emergency Controller to the presence of an incident by means of an audio and visual warning. The received SSR plot will show the precise location of the aircraft on the controller's radar display, and will then obviate the need for the emergency controller to carry out the more time-consuming manual aircraft position plotting procedure. Information on SSR operating procedures, including Special Purpose Codes 7700 (Emergency), 7600 (Radio Failure) and 7500 (Hijack or Other Act of Violence) are detailed in the ENR Section of the UK AIP.

9.5   EMERGENCY MESSAGE

9.5.1   The emergency message shall contain the following information (time and circumstance permitting) and, whenever possible, should be passed in the order given:

(a)   'MAYDAY/MAYDAY/MAYDAY' (or 'PAN PAN/PAN PAN/PAN PAN');

(b)   Name of the station addressed (when appropriate and time and circumstances permitting);

(c)   Callsign;

(d)   Type of aircraft;

(e)   Nature of the emergency;

(f)   Intention of the person-in-command;

(g)   Present or last known position, flight level/altitude and heading;

(h)   Pilot qualifications (See Note 1), viz:
(i)   Student pilots (see Note 2);
(ii)   No Instrument Qualification;
(iii)   IMC Rating;
(iv)   Full Instrument Rating.

(j)   Any other useful information eg endurance remaining, number of people on board (POB) etc.

Notes:

1   There is no ICAO requirement to include pilot qualifications in a distress message. However, this information should be included whenever possible in UK emergency messages as it may help the controller to plan a course of action best suited to the pilot's ability.

2   Inexperienced civil pilots are invited to use the callsign prefix 'TYRO' when in communication with a military unit or the D&D Section to indicate their lack of experience. Upon hearing this code word, military controllers will ensure that they do not issue complex instructions which the pilot could have difficulty in following.

3   POB – Total number of People on Board.

MAYDAY MAYDAY MAYDAY Milthorpe Tower G-ABCD Slingsby engine fire losing height intend an immediate forced landing 20 miles south of Milthorpe. Passing 3000 feet heading 360 PPL no instrument qualification 1 POB	G-ABCD Milthorpe Tower roger MAYDAY ..... (any pertinent information)
MAYDAY MAYDAY MAYDAY Milthorpe Tower G-ABCD C172 engine failed. Will attempt to land Milthorpe, 10 miles south, 4000 ft heading 360 Student pilot	G-ABCD Milthorpe Tower roger MAYDAY cleared straight-in runway 35 wind 260 10 knots QFE 1008 you are number one

9.6   SPEECHLESS CODE

9.6.1   If an emergency message received by the Military Emergency Controller is weak or distorted to the point of being unintelligible, the pilot may be asked to adopt the Speechless Code. This entails the pilot pressing his transmit button a certain number of times and using carrier wave only transmissions which, by convention, have the following code meanings:

Number of transmissions	Meaning
One Short	'Yes' or an acknowledgement
Two Short	'No'
Three Short	'Say again' (to be used by the pilot when he has not fully heard the controller's transmission, or has not understood the transmission, or the transmission was an instruction and the pilot is unable to comply).
Four Short (letter H in morse)	'Request Homing' (to an airfield), or used for initial alerting. (A civil pilot should only use the four short transmissions if he is aware, or suspects before attempting to make initial contact with the Emergency Controller, that his own aircraft microphone is unserviceable. The Emergency Controller will then interrogate the pilot, using the callsign 'Speechless Aircraft' if the identity of the aircraft is unknown).
One Long (2 secs)	'Manoeuvre Complete' (eg steady on heading).
One Long, Two Short and One Long (–..–) (letter X in morse)	'My aircraft has developed another emergency'

9.6.2 An aircraft SSR transponder can also be used, during times of communication difficulties, by a pilot to acknowledge or respond to messages by the transmission of SSR Code changes or squawking 'Ident' as requested by the controller.

9.6.3   If neither the state of DISTRESS nor URGENCY applies, a service is available at lower priority to pilots who find themselves in DIFFICULTY. Such pilots should make their situation clear and then provide as much information as possible to the emergency controller from the list at para 9.5.1 (a) to (j).

9.7   RADIO PROCEDURES – PRACTICE EMERGENCIES

9.7.1   Pilots may simulate emergency incidents (BUT NOT THE STATE OF DISTRESS) on 121.50 MHz to enable them to gain experience of the ATC service provided. Before calling, pilots should listen out on the emergency frequency to ensure that no actual or practice incident is already in progress. Practice calls need not disrupt a planned flight or involve additional expense in fuel or time since the pilot can request 'diversion' to his intended destination or cancel the exercise when necessary. Simulated emergency calls must be prefixed 'PRACTICE' and should be brief, eg:

> 'PRACTICE PAN, PRACTICE PAN, PRACTICE PAN,
> LONDON CENTRE G-ABCD'

The Emergency Controller will then indicate acceptance of the Practice Pan by transmitting:

> G-ABCD, LONDON CENTRE CONTINUE WITH
> PRACTICE PAN'

The Emergency Controller may instruct the pilot to call at another time, if the practice cannot be accommodated.

9.7.2   If a practice is accepted, the pilot should then pass his details. SSR Mode A Code 7700 should *not* be selected during a practice emergency exercise unless required by the Emergency Controller. Mode C should be switched on, if available.

9.8 TRAINING FIX

Pilots who do not wish to carry out a practice emergency but only wish to confirm their position may request a 'Training Fix' on 121.5 MHz. This 'Training Fix' is secondary in importance to actual emergency calls but takes precedence over practice emergency calls in the event of simultaneous incidents.

(Listen out before transmitting)

Training Fix, Training Fix, Training Fix, G-ABCD	G-ABCD, Scottish Centre your position is 7 miles south of Pitlochry

9.9 RELAYED EMERGENCY MESSAGE

9.9.1 Any aeronautical station or aircraft knowing of an emergency incident may transmit a distress message whenever such action is necessary to obtain assistance for the aircraft or vessel in distress. In such circumstances, it should be made clear that the aircraft transmitting is not itself in distress.

MAYDAY MAYDAY MAYDAY Milthorpe Tower G-ABCD have intercepted MAYDAY from G-BJRD I say again G-BJRD Cessna 172 engine failure forced landing 10 miles west of Wicken VOR, 1000 feet descending, heading 120, IMC rating, over	G-ABCD Milthorpe Tower Roger your relayed MAYDAY from G-BJRD

9.10 IMPOSITION OF SILENCE

9.10.1 Transmissions from aircraft in distress have priority over all other transmissions. On hearing an distress call, all stations must maintain radio silence on that frequency unless they themselves are required to render assistance and should continue to listen on the frequency concerned until it is evident that assistance is being provided. Stations should take care not to interfere with the transmission of urgency calls.

9.10.2 The aircraft in distress or the station in control of a distress incident may impose silence either on all stations in the area or on any particular station that interferes with distress transmissions. In either case, the message should take the following form:

> All stations Milthorpe Tower
> stop transmitting. MAYDAY

> or

> G-ABCD stop transmitting.
> MAYDAY

9.10.3 The aeronautical station acknowledging a distress message on a particular frequency may consider it prudent to transfer other aircraft from that frequency in order to avoid any disruption of transmission from or to the emergency aircraft.

> MAYDAY G-BJRD. All other
> aircraft contact Milthorpe
> Tower on 123.8, out

9.11 CANCELLATION OF EMERGENCY COMMUNICATIONS AND RT SILENCE

9.11.1 When an aircraft is no longer in distress it shall transmit a message cancelling the emergency condition.

> Milthorpe Tower G-BJRD
> cancel MAYDAY, engine
> restarted, runway in sight.
> Request landing

> G-RD cleared to land
> runway 35. Surface wind
> 320 6

> Cleared to land runway 35
> G-RD

9.11.2   When an distress incident has been resolved, the station which has been controlling the emergency traffic will transmit a message indicating that normal working may be resumed.

> All stations Milthorpe Tower
> MAYDAY traffic ended

Chapter 10 – Transmission of Aerodrome Information

10.1 METEOROLOGICAL INFORMATION

10.1.1 Meteorological information in the form of reports, forecasts or warnings is made available to pilots using the aeronautical mobile service either by broadcast (eg VOLMET) or by means of specific transmissions from ground personnel to pilots. Standard meteorological abbreviations and terms should be used and the information should be transmitted slowly and enunciated clearly in order that the recipient may record such data as is necessary.

> G-CD Borton Tower 0950
> weather surface wind
> 360 degrees 5 knots visibility
> 30 kms. Nil weather, 2 oktas
> 2500 feet temperature
> plus 10, dew point plus 3,
> QNH 1010

> QNH 1010 G-CD

Note: Cloud may also be reported as follows:

'Scattered at five hundred feet, scattered cumulonimbus at one thousand feet, broken at two thousand five hundred feet.'

In the above example 'scattered' equates to 3 or 4 Octas and 'broken' equates to 5–7 Octas.

Full details of meteorological information is contained in UK AIP GEN section.

10.2 VOICE WEATHER BROADCAST (VOLMET) UK

10.2.1 Meteorological aerodrome reports for certain aerodromes are broadcast on specified frequencies. The callsign of the VOLMET, frequency, operating hours, aerodromes contained within the group, and contents are published in the UK AIP.

10.2.2 The content of a VOLMET broadcast is as follows:

(a)   Aerodrome identification (eg Stourton)

(b)   Surface wind

(c)   Visibility (Note 1)

(d)   RVR (if applicable) (Note 1)

(e)   Weather

(f)   Cloud (Note 1)

(g)   Temperature

(h)   Dewpoint

(i)   QNH

(j)   Trend (if applicable)

Notes: 1   Non essential words such as 'surface wind', 'visibility' etc
             are not spoken.
         2   'SNOCLO' is used to indicate that aerodrome is unusable
             for take-off/landings due to heavy snow on runways or
             snow clearance.
         3   All broadcasts are in English.

10.3   RUNWAY VISUAL RANGE (RVR)/VISIBILITY/ABSOLUTE MINIMUM

10.3.1   When transmitting the runway visual range the abbreviation RVR will
be used without using the phonetic word for each letter, eg RVR
runway 27, 800 metres. The runway designator may be omitted if there
is no possibility of confusion.

10.3.2   Where instrumented runway visual range (IRVR) observations are
available, more than one reading may be transmitted.

Fastair 345 RVR runway 27 650 600 600	Fastair 345
Fastair 345 RVR runway 27 touchdown 650 stop end 550	Fastair 345

134

10.3.3   In the UK, there is an approach ban which states that a pilot may not continue an instrument approach beyond the outer marker, or equivalent position, if the reported RVR, or at aerodromes where RVR measurements are not taken or available, the visibility, is below the minimum specified for that approach. Essentially, this means that a pilot may not descend below 1,000 feet above the aerodrome when these conditions exist. This RVR/visibility is known as an 'absolute minimum'.

10.3.4   Should a pilot indicate that he or she intends to commence an instrument approach when the reported RVR/visibility is less than the notified 'absolute minimum' value, the controller should inform the pilot using the following RT phraseology:

> Fastair 345 you are advised
> that the current RVR/visibility
> is (number) metres which is
> below the absolute minimum
> for a (name) approach to
> runway (number). What are
> your intentions?

10.4   RUNWAY SURFACE CONDITIONS

10.4.1   When conditions of standing water, with or without reports of braking action, are brought to the attention of a controller, the available information will be passed to aircraft likely to be affected.

10.4.2   Information on standing water will be passed in general descriptive terms, for example 'damp', 'wet', 'water patches' or 'flooded' according to the amount of water present.

10.4.3   When suitable equipment is available reports of braking action on wet runways will be passed to pilots.

10.4.4   Other runway surface conditions which may be of concern to a pilot will be passed by ATC.

| Fastair 345 braking action medium, heavy rain time of measurement 0830 | Fastair 345 |

| Fastair 345 displaced threshold runway 27 500 feet due broken surface | Fastair 345 |

10.5 AUTOMATIC TERMINAL INFORMATION SERVICE (ATIS) UK

10.5.1 To alleviate RT loading at some busy airports, Automatic Terminal Information Service (ATIS) messages are broadcast to pass routine arrival/departure information on a discrete RT frequency or on an appropriate VOR. Pilots inbound to these airports are normally required on first contact with the aerodrome ATSU to acknowledge receipt of current information by quoting the code letter of the broadcast. Pilots of outbound aircraft are not normally required to acknowledge receipt of departure ATIS except when requested on the actual ATIS broadcast. If, however, pilots report receipt of a departure ATIS broadcast the QNH should be included thereby allowing ATC to check that the quoted QNH is up-to-the-minute.

10.5.2 Aerodromes possessing ATIS, the hours of ATIS operation and the frequency employed are published in the UK AIP.

10.5.3 ATIS broadcasts which should be no more than thirty seconds duration, will include the following:

(a) Message identification ie 'This is Stourton Information Alpha'. Each message is consecutively coded using the phonetic alphabet.

(b) Time of origin of weather report.

(c) Weather report (see para 10.2.2(a)–(c)).

(d) Runway(s) in use.

(e) Short term AIS information such as unserviceability of NAV AIDS, runway surfaces etc.

(f)   Any other routine information useful to pilots operating at the aerodrome.

Notes: 1 RVR/RVRs are not included, however, IRVRs may be available where approved.
2 Rapidly changing meteorological situations sometimes make it impractical to include weather reports in the broadcast. In these circumstances, ATIS messages will indicate that weather information will be passed on RT.
3 Any significant change to the content of a current ATIS message will be passed to pilots by RT until such time as a new message is broadcast.
4 The highest cloud base that will be reported is 10000 feet.

10.5.4   Example of ATIS broadcast:

'This is Stourton Approach Information Alpha. 0850 hours weather. 240° 12 kts. 10 km. Intermittent slight rain. Scattered at 1000 ft, overcast at 1800 ft. Temperature +12. Dew point +7. QNH 1011 mbs. Landing runway 28. Report information Alpha received on first contact with Stourton.'

Note: A Trend may be included in an ATIS broadcast.

Chapter 11 – Miscellaneous Flight Handling

11.1 WAKE VORTEX

11.1.1 ATC will provide the appropriate spacing between IFR flights but, if a pilot elects to execute a visual approach, or is operating as a VFR flight, it is his responsibility to provide adequate spacing, although ATC will pass the appropriate distance.

> G-BJCD caution vortex wake the recommended spacing is (number) miles

> G-BJCD

11.2 WIND SHEAR

11.2.1 When wind shear is forecast or is reported by aircraft, ATC will warn other aircraft until such time as aircraft report the phenomenon no longer exists.

> G-CD at 0745 a departing B757 reported windshear at 800 feet. Airspeed loss 20 kts, strong right drift

11.3 AIRPROX REPORTING

11.3.1 An AIRPROX Report should be made by any pilot flying in the United Kingdom Flight Information Region, the Upper Flight Information Region or Shanwick Oceanic Area when in his opinion, the distance between aircraft as well as their relative positions and speed have been such that the safety of the aircraft involved was or may have been compromised.

11.3.2 The initial report is made by RT to the ATSU in communication with the aircraft except that if the controllers workload is such that he is not able to accept the report the pilot will be requested to file details after landing.

11.3.3 The Pilot's RT report should commence with words 'AIRPROX REPORT' and should include the following items:

Aircraft Callsign

SSR Code

Position of AIRPROX

Aircraft heading

Flight level, altitude or height

Altimeter setting

Aircraft attitude (level/climbing/descending/turning)

Weather conditions

Date and time (UTC) of the AIRPROX

Description of other aircraft

First sighting distance and details of flight paths of reporting and reported aircraft.

11.3.4 RT AIRPROX reports are to be confirmed in writing within seven days of the incident to allow follow up action to be taken. (See UK AIP ENR Section.)

11.4   OIL POLLUTION REPORTING

11.4.1 Pilots sighting substantial patches of oil are requested to make reports by RT to the ATSU with whom they are in communication or the appropriate FIS in order that action can be taken.

The RT reports should contain the following:

'OIL POLLUTION REPORT' OR 'POLLUTION REPORT'

. . . Time and date (if required) pollution was observed and identify of reporting aircraft.

. . . Position and extent of pollution

. . . Tide, windspeed and direction

. . . Weather conditions and Sea state

. . . Characteristics of pollution

... Name and nationality or description, including any distinctive markings, of any vessel seen discharging oil or other harmful substances; also estimated course and speed of vessel and if pollution is observed ahead of the discharging ship and the estimated length of pollution in her wake

... Identity of any other vessels in the immediate vicinity

... Whether photographs taken.

11.5 INTERCEPTIONS BY MILITARY AIRCRAFT

Pilots are warned that should they become involved in an interception by military aircraft they should follow the international procedures as detailed in the UK AIP ENR Section.

11.6 AIRCRAFT OPERATING AGENCY MESSAGES

11.6.1 Aircraft operating agency radio stations may only transmit and receive flight regularity and flight safety messages.

11.6.2 Flight regularity messages comprise the following:

(a) Messages regarding the operation or maintenance of facilities essential for the safety or regularity of aircraft operation.

(b) Messages concerning the servicing of aircraft.

(c) Instructions to aircraft operating agency representatives concerning changes in requirements for passengers and crew caused by unavoidable deviations from normal operating schedules. Individual requirements of passengers or crew are not admissible in this type of message.

(d) Messages concerning non-routine landings to be made by the aircraft.

(e) Messages concerning aircraft parts and materials urgently required.

(f) Messages concerning changes in aircraft operating schedules.

11.6.3   Flight safety messages include the following:

(a)   Messages originated by an aircraft operating agency, or by an aircraft, of immediate concern to an aircraft in flight.

(b)   Meteorological advice of immediate concern to an aircraft in flight or about to depart.

11.6.4   It is permissible for aircraft operating agency messages to be handled by the aerodrome communication facility provided this can be achieved without interference with its primary role and no other channels are available for the handling of such messages.

11.6.5   Public correspondence messages are not permitted on VHF frequencies in the aeronautical mobile service.

11.7   8.33 kHz PHRASEOLOGY

11.7.1   As an interim solution to severe VHF spectrum congestion ICAO has split the VHF communications band from 25 kHz to 8.33 kHz channel spacing. 8.33 kHz frequencies are referred to as 'channels'. There is a sixth digit at the end of the channel designation and when transferring between channels all six digits must be used. The following phraseology shall only be used when referring to 8.33 kHz channels.

Circumstances	Phraseology
To request the capability of the radio equipment	Advise eight point[1] three three equipped
To indicate 8.33 kHz capability	*Affirm/Negative eight point three three
To indicate UHF capability	*UHF equipped
To request the status in respect of exemption	*(aircraft call sign) exempted eight point three three

*Denotes pilot transmission

Example: 'Fastair 345 contact Wrayton Control channel 132.010'. The channel would be spoken as '... one three two decimal zero one zero'.

[1] Note use of 'point' instead of 'decimal' when referring to '8.33'.

142

Circumstances	Phraseology
To indicate that a certain clearance is given because otherwise a non-equipped aircraft would enter the airspace of mandatory carriage	(clearance/instruction) due eight point three three requirement
To request the pilot to confirm the 8.33 kHz selection	(a) Confirm eight point three three channel (b*)Affirm eight point three three channel (name)
Transfer of control and/or channel change	(a) Contact (unit call sign) channel (name) (b) At/Over (time or place) contact (unit call sign) channel (name) (c) If no contact (instructions) (d) Stand by channel (name) for (unit call sign)[2] (e*)Request change to channel (name) (f) Channel change approved (g) Monitor (unit call sign) channel (name) (h*)Monitoring channel (name) (i) When ready contact (unit call sign) channel (name) (j) Remain this channel

*Denotes pilot transmission

Example: 'Fastair 345 contact Wrayton Control channel 132.010'. The channel would be spoken as '... one three two decimal zero one zero'.

[2] This phraseology is not generally used in the UK as 'Monitor (unit call sign) channel (name)' serves the same purpose.

Chapter 12 – Examples of an IFR Flight and a VFR/IFR Flight

12.1 INTRODUCTION

12.1.1 An example of an IFR flight from one major airport to another, and an example of a VFR flight from a provincial aerodrome to a landing site, are given in graphic form in this chapter. The latter then changes to an IFR flight on departure again to illustrate the differences between RAS and RIS (see Chapter 7). As before the agency making the initial call is on the left-hand side of the page; thereafter messages connected with the subject appear in colour-coded chronological order but on the *relative* side of the page. The agencies can be identified as follows:

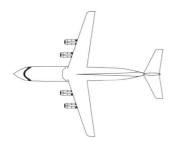

FASTAIR 345

G-ABCD

GROUND/TOWER/APPROACH

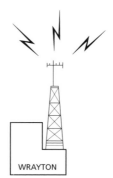

WRAYTON ACC (CONTROL/INFORMATION)

12.2 AN IFR FLIGHT

12.2.1 Start up

Stourton Ground Fastair 345 radio check 118.3	Station calling Stourton Ground say again your callsign
Stourton Ground Fastair 345. Radio check 118.3	Fastair 345 Stourton Ground readability 5.
Ground Fastair 345, stand 24, information bravo, QNH 1011 request start up	Fastair 345 start up *approved*

Note: APPROVED used-not CLEAR/CLEARED.

12.2.2 Clearance

Fastair 345 is *cleared* to Kennington via A1 at FL 60, request level change en-route, squawk 5501

Cleared to Kennington at FL 60, request level change en-route, squawk 5501 Fastair 345

Fastair 345 correct

Notes: 1   The word CLEARED is introduced.
        2   A full readback of a clearance is required – see para 12.2.4.

Ground Fastair 345 request pushback

Fastair 345 pushback *approved*

Note: APPROVED – NOT CLEAR

Ground Fastair 345 information Charlie QNH 1011 request taxi

Fastair 345 taxi to holding point runway 24

Taxi to holding point runway 24 Fastair 345

Fastair 345 contact Stourton Tower 118.9

Stourton Tower 118.9 Fastair 345

Note: Full readback of taxi clearance as the message contains the runway in use – see para 2.7.5.5.

12.2.4 Pre-departure and Take-off

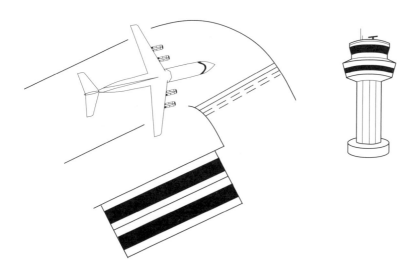

Stourton Tower Fastair 345
ready for *departure*

Fastair 345 Stourton Tower
after *departure* climb
straight ahead until passing
altitude 2500 feet

After *departure* climb
straight ahead until passing
altitude 2500 feet Fastair 345

Fastair 345 *line up and wait.*
Vehicle crossing upwind end
of runway

Line up and wait. Fastair 345

Notes: 1   'DEPARTURE' employed and not 'TAKE-OFF'.
        2   'CLEARED' is not used in these cases – see next 'Notes'.
        3   Full readback is required for instructions to ENTER, LAND,
           TAKE-OFF ON, BACKTRACK, HOLD SHORT OF, OR
           CROSS a runway.
        4   'LINE UP AND WAIT' (plus reason) is employed; 'LINE UP'
           (only) may also be used.

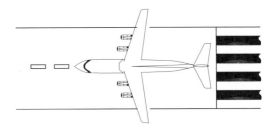

Fastair 345 cleared take-off
surface wind calm

Cleared take-off Fastair 345

Notes: 1 TAKE-OFF – these words are *only* used when an aircraft is
           cleared for TAKE-OFF.
        2 TAKE-OFF clearance requires readback.
        3 Use of CLEAR is restricted to:
           (i)   ATC clearances.
           (ii)   Departure and Approach instructions.
           (iii) Take-off and landing clearances.

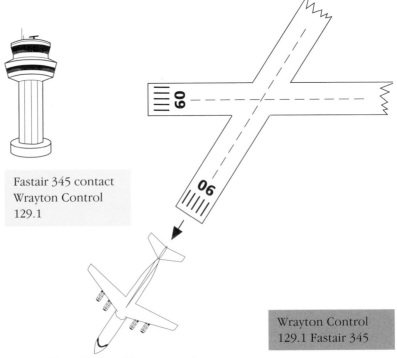

Fastair 345 contact
Wrayton Control
129.1

Wrayton Control
129.1 Fastair 345

Note: Full readback of frequency change.

12.2.5 En-Route

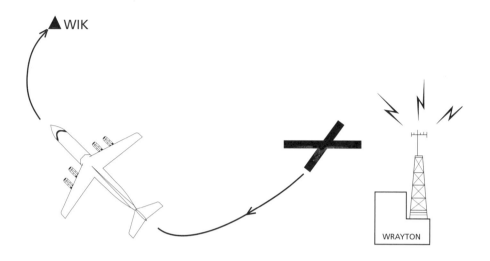

Wrayton Control Fastair 345
passing altitude 3000 feet
Stourton QNH 1011 turning
inbound Wicken climbing
FL 60 requesting FL 280

Fastair 345 Wrayton Control
climb FL 280 report reaching

Climbing FL 280 Wilco
Fastair 345

Notes: 1 Full readback of level instruction.
       2 REPORT instruction employed.

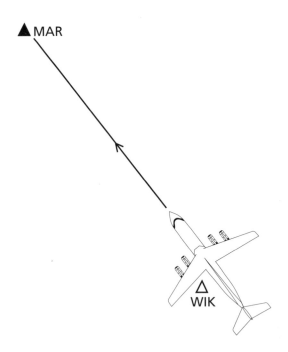

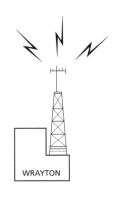

WRAYTON

Fastair 345 Wicken 47 FL 130 climbing FL 280 Marlow 07

Fastair 345 Roger

Note: Position report consists of:

(a) Aircraft identification.
(b) Position.
(c) Time.
(d) Level.
(e) Next position and ETA.

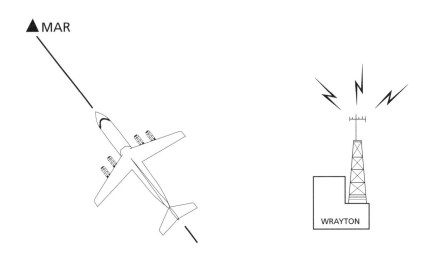

▲MAR

WRAYTON

Fastair 345 reaching FL 280 | Fastair 345

Note: For passing instructions/reports regarding height/altitude or flight level, use CLIMB(ING), DESCEND(ING), PASSING, REACHING or LEAVING but *not* CLEARED/RE-CLEARED.

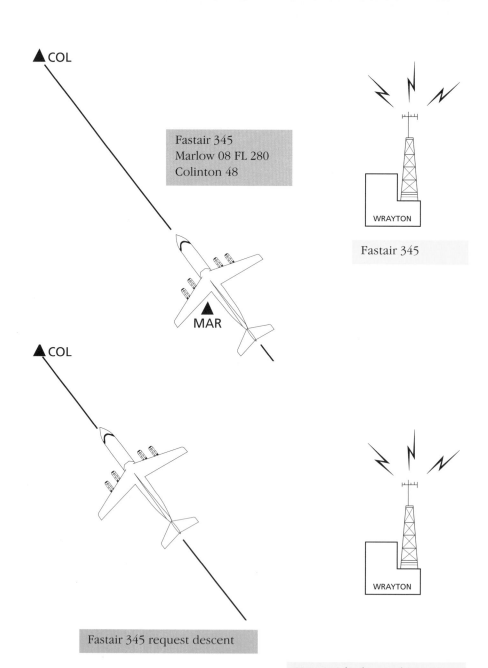

COL

Fastair 345
Marlow 08 FL 280
Colinton 48

MAR

WRAYTON

Fastair 345

COL

Fastair 345 request descent

WRAYTON

Fastair 345 descend FL 120
cross Colinton FL 170 or
above

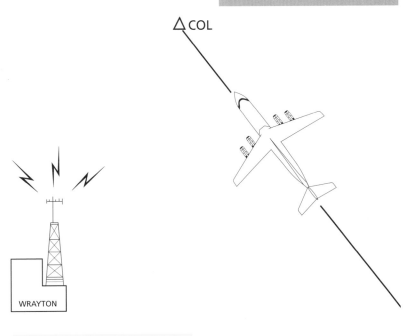

Descending FL 120 will cross
Colinton FL 170 or above
Fastair 345

△COL

WRAYTON

Fastair 345 report your level

Fastair 345 passing FL 225

Fastair 345 Roger. Are you
able to cross Colinton at time
52

Affirm. Fastair 345

Fastair 345 cross Colinton not
before time 52

Cross Colinton not before 52
Fastair 345

Note: AFFIRM(ative)/NEGATIVE are used when a question requires a
direct answer. Therefore, ROGER is not used in this case.

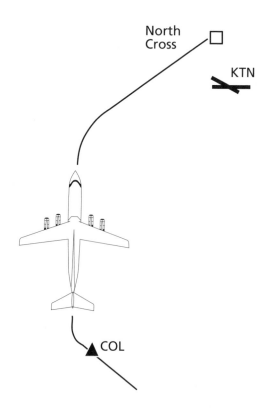

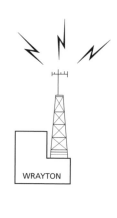

Fastair 345 Colinton 52
FL 180 descending FL 120
request direct North Cross
for ILS approach at
Kennington

Fastair 345 Roger. Route
direct to North Cross.
Descend FL 60. Report West
abeam KTN

Direct North Cross descend
FL 60. Wilco Fastair 345

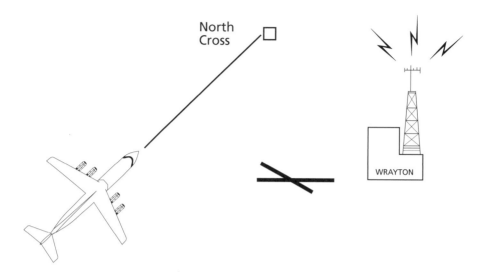

Fastair 345 West abeam
Kennington 03 FL 110
descending FL 60 North
Cross 11

Fastair 345 Roger. Contact
Kennington Approach 119.7

Kennington Approach 119.7
Fastair 345

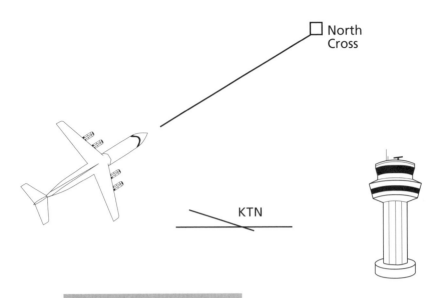

North
Cross

KTN

Kennington Approach Fastair
345 FL 90 descending FL 60
approaching North Cross
information Golf

Fastair 345 Kennington
Approach vectoring for ILS
approach runway 28

ILS RW 28 Fastair 345

Fastair 345 Leave North
Cross heading 120

Leave North Cross heading
120 Fastair 345

Note: Full readback of HEADING (and speed) instructions; also
runway identifier.

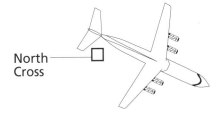

North
Cross

Fastair 345 North Cross FL 60
heading 120

Fastair 345 descend to
altitude 2500 feet QNH 1011

Descend to altitude 2500 feet
QNH 1011 Fastair 345

Fastair 345 position 10 miles
northeast of Kennington

Fastair 345

Fastair 345 turn right
heading 190 base leg
14 miles northeast of
Kennington

Right heading 190 Fastair 345

Fastair 345 turn right heading 240

Right heading 240 Fastair 345

Fastair 345 closing final approach track from the right 12 miles from touchdown

Fastair 345

Fastair 345 closing the localiser from the right, report established

Wilco Fastair 345

Fastair 345 localiser established

Fastair 345 descend on the ILS QFE 1008

QFE 1008, wilco Fastair 345

Fastair 345 contact Tower 118.9

Tower 118.9 Fastair 345

160

Kennington Tower
Fastair 345 long final RW 28

Fastair 345 Kennington Tower
cleared to land runway 28
surface wind 240 10

Cleared to land runway 28
Fastair 345

Note: Surface wind: 'Degrees' and 'Knots' may be omitted.

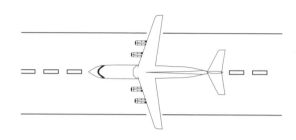

Fastair 345 *vacate*
convenient right

Vacate right Fastair 345

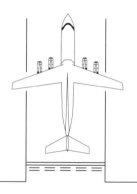

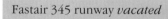

Fastair 345 runway *vacated*

Note: VACATE runway and *not* CLEAR runway.

12.3 A VFR/IFR FLIGHT

12.3.1 This particular example is aimed at the pilot flying outside regulated airspace under services provided by the military in the UK (Westbury) to show the slight differences that exist from civil ATS as portrayed in previous chapters.

12.3.2 **Engine Start and Departure Information**

Borton Tower G-ABCD radio check 118.7	G-ABCD Borton Tower readability 5
Borton Tower G-ABCD Slingsby T67 starting, request departure information	G-CD departure runway 24 surface wind 220 6, QNH 990 millibars temperature +6 dew point +3
Runway 24 QNH 997 millibars G-CD	G-CD negative. QNH 990 millibars
QNH 990 millibars G-CD	
Borton Tower G-ABCD, T67 at the south side hangars request taxi for VFR flight to Walden	G-CD taxy to holding point runway 24 via taxiway Charlie QNH 990 millibars
Holding point runway 24 via taxiway Charlie QNH 990 millibars, request surface wind G-CD	G-CD surface wind calm
G-CD request departure on runway 14	G-CD taxy to holding point runway 14
Taxy to holding point runway 14 G-CD	

12.3.3 Pre-departure and Take-off

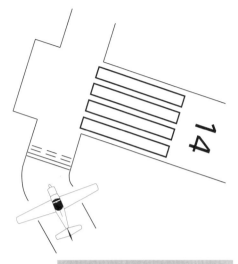

G-CD ready for *departure* request left turnout heading 330

G-CD, left turn *approved*. After departure climb not above altitude 2500 feet until reaching the zone boundary

Left turn approved. Not above altitude 2500 feet until zone boundary G-CD

G-CD cleared take-off runway 14 surface wind 220 4

Cleared take-off runway 14 G-CD

Notes: 1 DEPARTURE used not TAKE-OFF.
2 APPROVED used not CLEARED.
3 Full readback of departure clearance.
4 Runway identified as in this case it is not the runway in use.
5 Readback of take-off clearance.

163

12.3.4 Post Departure

G-CD contact Borton
Approach 118.75

Borton Approach 118.75
G-CD

Borton Approach G-ABCD
airborne runway 14 turning
left heading 330 climbing to
altitude 2500 feet QNH 990
millibars, en-route Walden

G-CD Roger. *Report* reaching
2500 feet

Wilco G-CD

G-CD reaching altitude
2500 feet

G-CD Roger *report* at the
zone boundary

Wilco G-CD

G-CD zone boundary
changing to Wrayton
Information 125.75

G-CD Roger, Regional
Pressure Setting 988 millibars

Regional Pressure Setting 988
millibars G-CD

Notes: 1   REPORT introduced.
         2   CHANGING TO announces intention to change frequency.

12.3.5 **En-route**

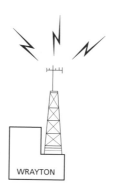

WRAYTON

Wrayton Information
G-ABCD request Flight
Information Service

> G-ABCD Wrayton
> Information pass your
> message

Wrayton G-ABCD T67 from
Borton 15 miles northwest of
Borton heading 330,
climbing FL 45, VFR
destination Walden

> G-CD Roger. Flight
> Information Service

G-CD Flight Information,
maintaining FL 45

> G-CD

Wrayton G-CD request VHF
frequency for Westbury
Approach

> G-CD Westbury Approach
> 119.7

Wrayton Information G-CD
descending due weather.
Changing to Westbury
Approach for LARS

> G-CD regional pressure
> setting 988 millibars

Regional pressure setting 988
millibars G-CD

12.3.6 Lower Airspace Radar Service and MATZ Penetration Service

Note: Westbury is a military unit.

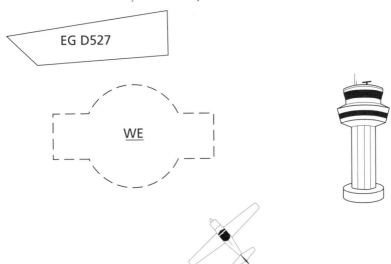

Westbury Approach G-ABCD request Lower Airspace Radar Service

G-CD Westbury Approach pass your message

Westbury G-CD Slingsby T67, from Borton, 20 miles southeast of Westbury, heading 340, FL 40 descending to altitude 2500 feet regional regional pressure 988 millibars, VFR en-route Walden requesting Radar Information Service

G-CD squawk 6512

6512 G-CD

G-CD identified 16 miles southeast of Westbury. Radar Information. Report reaching 2500 feet

Radar Information, Wilco. G-CD request MATZ penetration

G-CD Roger

Note: Details of LARS and MATZ Penetration Service can be found in the UK AIP, AICs and Temporary Supplements.

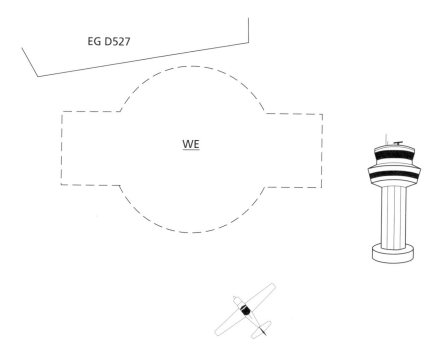

EG D527

WE

G-CD request level

G-CD altitude 2900 feet

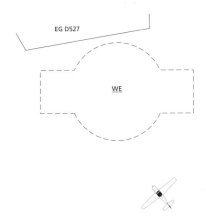

G-CD set Westbury QFE 981 millibars

Westbury QFE 981 millibars set G-CD

G-CD descend report level 1500 feet for MATZ penetration

Descend report level height 1500 feet G-CD

G-CD reaching 1500 feet

G-CD maintain 1500 feet MATZ penetration approved

Wilco, MATZ penetration approved G-CD

Note: Military controllers do not apply the conventions relating to the use of altitude/height clearances as described at para 3.2.3(b).

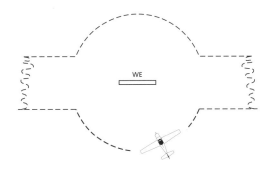

G-CD entering MATZ limited warning of traffic from ahead as you approach my radar overhead

G-CD Roger. Request join for one visual circuit

G-CD Roger. Standby

G-CD one visual circuit approved maintain 1500 ft to overhead. Do you have the field in sight?

Maintain 1500 ft to overhead. G-CD has the field in sight

G-CD roger. Runway 27 right hand circuit height 1000 feet QFE 981 millibars

Runway 27 right hand circuit height 1000 feet QFE 981 millibars G-CD

G-CD what is your POB

G-CD 1 POB

G-CD contact Westbury Tower 132.85, radar service terminated

Westbury Tower 132.85 G-CD

Notes: 1 The question of landing fees etc is not addressed in this scenario.
2 Circuit direction is only given when circuit is not left-hand.
3 Military units employ QFE in the circuit area, the instrument pattern and for MATZ penetration.
4 POB – Total number of People on Board.

12.3.7 The Military Visual Circuit

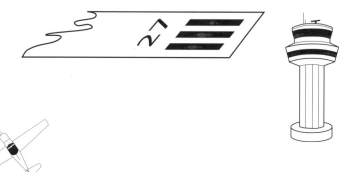

Westbury Tower G-ABCD 2 miles southeast height 1500 ft QFE 981 millibars to join for one visual circuit

G-CD Westbury Tower join overhead at 1500 feet for runway 27 right hand QFE 981 millibars circuit clear

Join overhead 1500 feet
runway 27 right hand
QFE 981 millibars G-CD

G-CD overhead 1500 feet

G-CD report downwind at
1000 feet one fast jet joining
base leg to land

G-CD Wilco

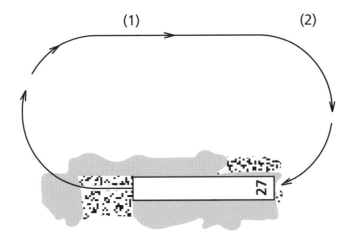

(1) (2)

Military Rectangular Visual Circuit Pattern

Notes: 1 Downwind report is made abeam upwind end of runway.
Aircraft intentions are stated here.
2 'Finals' call is made *just before turning base leg*.
3 Military (jet) circuits tend to be relatively tight and are
more oval-shaped.
4 Military use 'two in', 'three in' etc for number of aircraft
present in the visual circuit.

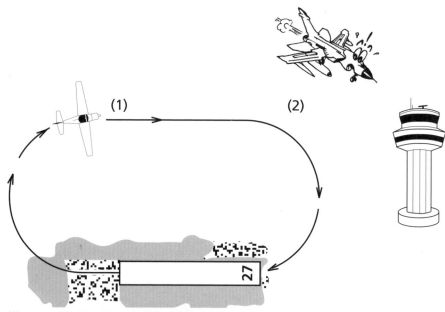

(1) G-CD downwind 1000 feet
request touch and go then
depart to the northwest.
Request Danger Area
Crossing Service of EGD512

G-CD surface wind 250 5 one
ahead to land. DACS request
copied

(2) G-CD final gear down

G-CD go around 500 feet
deadside one on remaining

Go around 500 ft deadside
G-CD

Notes: 1   Surface wind is passed at downwind position.
2   An aircraft with retractable undercarriage will be expected
to call 'gear down'or three greens with the final call.
3   Military use 'Roll' for 'Touch and Go'.
4   'Go Around' see para 4.10.4.
5   Military use 'Overshoot' for 'Low Approach'.

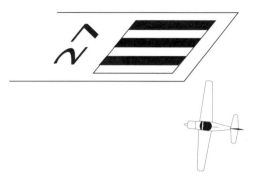

G-CD at upwind end of runway turn right heading 290 climb to 2000 feet QFE 981 millibars

Upwind end of runway right heading 290 climb to height 2000 feet QFE 981 millibars G-CD

G-CD heading 290 climbing to height 2000 feet

G-CD contact Westbury Approach 119.7

Westbury Approach 119.7 G-CD

Note: Full readback of clearance and frequency change.

12.3.8 LARS and DACS

Westbury Approach G-ABCD heading 290 maintaining height 2000 ft QFE 981 millibars now IFR requesting Radar Advisory Service

G-CD Westbury Approach squawk ident. What is your requested level?

Ident G-CD. Request FL45

G-CD identified, Radar Advisory, EGD527 Loudwater active will you accept a re-route?

Radar Advisory, affirm G-CD

G-CD maintain heading 290 climb FL45

Heading 290 climbing FL 45 G-CD

Notes: 1 AFFIRM used.
        2 Military controllers use 'MAINTAIN' heading.

174

EG D527

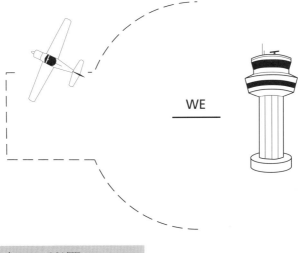

WE

G-CD leaving MATZ

G-CD

G-CD reaching FL 45

G-CD Roger I will be turning
you right in 7 miles to regain
track

G-CD

Note: Report leaving a MATZ.

12.3.9 Avoiding Action

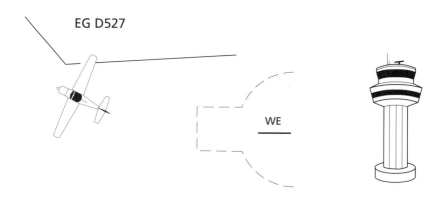

EG D527

WE

G-CD avoiding action, turn left heading 230 pop-up traffic was 12 o'clock range 6 miles no height reciprocal heading

Left heading 230 G-CD

Notes: 1   This type of avoiding action when under Radar Advisory is given at the controller's discretion for late sighting/pop-up traffic.

2   Normally an avoiding action call as follows can be expected: G-CD traffic left 11 o'clock 6 miles height unknown crossing left to right, if not sighted turn left heading 230.

EG D527

WE

G-CD clear of traffic, turn right heading 340 direct for Walden

Right heading 340. Request change to Wrayton Information 125.75 G-CD

G-CD squawk Alpha 7000 Westbury terminating service

Alpha 7000 G-CD

12.3.10 En-Route/Flight Information Service

Wrayton Information
G-ABCD request Flight
Information Service

G-ABCD Wrayton Information
pass your message

Wrayton Information G-ABCD
T67 from Borton, 15 miles
northwest of Westbury
heading 340, FL 45, VFR, en-
route Walden, request
Walden weather

G-CD Roger Flight
Information Service, standby
for weather

Flight Information, G-CD

G-CD I have the Walden
weather are you ready to
copy

Affirm G-CD

G-CD Walden 0950 weather
runway 27, surface wind calm,
visibility 10 kilometres, nil
weather, few at 4000 feet,
scattered at 8000 feet, QNH
989 millibars temperature +4.
Dew point +1

G-CD changing to Wrayton
on 121.5 for Practice PAN

G-CD

12.3.11 **Practice Pan**

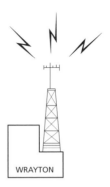

WRAYTON

(121.5 – listen out before transmitting)

Practice Pan, Practice Pan,
Practice Pan, Wrayton Centre
G-ABCD

G-ABCD this is Wrayton
Centre continue with Practice
Pan

Wrayton Centre G-ABCD,
Slingsby T67, simulating
rough running engine,
request diversion to nearest
aerodrome, 20 miles
northwest of Westbury, FL
45, turning right heading
140, IMC rating, one person
on board squawking Alpha
7000 with Charlie

G-ABCD Wrayton squawk
7301 ident

7301 ident G-ABCD

EG D

G-ABCD identified 17 miles northwest of Westbury, turn right heading 160 for Westbury for landing runway 09 surface wind 270 3 knots

Heading 160 for approach to runway 09 at Westbury G-ABCD

G-ABCD are you ready for Westbury weather, 13 miles northwest of Westbury

Wrayton Westbury weather not required cancelling Practice Pan G-ABCD

G-ABCD Roger. Practice Pan cancelled

G-ABCD changing to Walden 135.25

G-ABCD squawk A-7000

A-7000 G-ABCD

Note: Use of the VHF International Emergency Service is detailed in the UK AIP and AICs and Chapter 9.

12.3.12 **Arrival**

 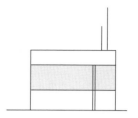

Walden Information G-ABCD inbound

G-ABCD Walden Information pass your message

G-ABCD T67, 6 miles southeast descending to height 1000 feet request joining information

G-CD runway 27 QFE 986 millibars 3 aircraft in circuit

Runway 27 QFE 986 millibars G-CD

G-CD joining left base

G-CD

G-CD final

G-CD runway occupied with a PA28, surface wind 260 6

G-CD runway now vacated, land at your discretion, surface wind 270 10

G-CD roger landing

G-CD runway vacated

G-CD

Notes: 1   *Joining Information* is requested and the pilot should position accordingly.

2   *Joining Instructions* are only issued where an **ATC** service is provided.

3   *When taking off or landing*, the pilot should state his intention when options are available eg landing/going around, taking off/holding position.

G-ABCD

Our thanks to Squadron Leader M J Setterfield RAF for the cartoons.

Bibliography

Titles

Books referred to in this publication are as follows:

ICAO Annex 10 Volume 2 – COMMUNICATION PROCEDURES
Reference No. AN10–2   Price £13.75

PANS-RAC Document 4444: PROCEDURES FOR AIR NAVIGATION SERVICES –
RULES OF THE AIR AND AIR TRAFFIC SERVICES
Reference No. 4444   Price £32.50

UK AIP (CAP 32): UNITED KINGDOM AERONAUTICAL INFORMATION
PUBLICATION   All 'ENR' references are contained herein.
Reference No. 6605   Price £570.00 (Paper format) £75.00 (CD format)

MATS (CAP 493): MANUAL OF AIR TRAFFIC SERVICES Reference No. 7506
Price £40.00

MFIS (CAP 410): MANUAL OF FLIGHT INFORMATION SERVICES
Reference No. 2325 Part A – General   Price £4.00
2326 Part B – Aerodrome   Price £4.50

Operators Guide (CAP 452): AERONAUTICAL RADIO STATION –
OPERATORS' GUIDE
Reference No. 2866   Price £3.75

NOTE: The above prices are valid at the time of going to press. Current prices
may be obtained by telephoning the number shown overleaf.

Methods of purchase

CAA and ICAO publications may be obtained from Westward documedia
Limited (WDL) by the following methods:

Post – Use Order Form at the end of the book or write order detailing reference
no., publication details, quantity required and cost per item(s). Add post and
packing charges plus VAT where applicable, and advise the method of payment to
be used.

Telephone – Orders are accepted by telephone at Westward documedia Limited (01242) 235151. Where payment is to be made by cheque then a written confirmation order must be sent together with the cheque.

Fax – Order forms or written orders are acceptable by fax at Westward documedia Limited (01242) 584139; but payment must be received before goods are despatched.

Proforma – In cases where costs are unknown or the request is not properly completed, a proforma may be raised detailing correct information and monies due before the order can proceed.

Cheques – Cheques to be made payable to Westward documedia Limited (written in full).

Credit Cards – Visa and Access credit cards are acceptable, also Switch for personal callers only. An order paid by this method may be by post, telephone or fax to Westward documedia Limited.

International Money Order – For overseas customers payment in sterling by International Money Order or Bank Draft drawn on a UK bank is required.

Personal callers – Personal callers are welcome to make purchases (by arrangement only). Please telephone to ensure that required publications are available as stocks may need to be obtained from our warehouse first and the method of payment agreed before goods can be collected. (See Publication Order Form at end of book for telephone number and address.)

Index

PUBLICATIONS ORDER FORM

Please supply the following publications:

REFERENCE NO.	DESCRIPTION	UNIT PRICE	QUANTITY	TOTAL PRICE
		PACKING AND POSTAGE		
		VAT (if applicable)		
		GRAND TOTAL		

CUSTOMER INFORMATION Please use BLOCK CAPITALS

Name _____

Address _____

_____

_____

Postcode _____ Daytime Tel No. _____

Signature _____ Date _____

POSTAGE AND PACKING RATES

	UK	Overseas (surface) and airmail,
Up to £10	£2.00	*please enquire*
over £10 up to £100	£4.00	

Orders over £100 will be subject to special rates depending on number of packages and costs involved.
VAT is applicable to the Postage and Packing charges where the goods supplied are Standard Rated.

METHOD OF PAYMENT

(a) Remittance for £ _____ is enclosed (Cheque/Postal Order/Money Order payable to Westward Digital Limited).

or only

(b) Please debit my credit card no: ⬚⬚⬚⬚⬚⬚⬚⬚⬚⬚⬚⬚ expiry date ⬚⬚⬚⬚

(c) Telephone orders may be made to MAIL ORDER SECTION – Cheltenham (01242) 235151.

(d) Overseas customers are requested to pay by a sterling draft drawn on a UK Bank or International Money Order in sterling.

Please ensure all parts of this Order Form have been completed correctly and despatch to:

Westward documedia Limited, 37 Windsor Street, Cheltenham, Glos. GL52 2DG, England. Telephone Cheltenham (01242) 235151.